THE NEW OFFICIAL CHECK LIST AND GRADING GUIDE U. S. COINS

**ALL GRADES WITH MINTAGE FIGURES
1793 TO DATE
VISUAL POINTERS ON HOW TO
GRADE EACH ISSUE.**

*Includes—All Regular and Commemorative Issues,
Complete Mint Records.*

AN OFFICIAL PUBLICATION OF:
DAFRAN HOUSE PUBLISHERS
25 West 39th Street, N.Y., N.Y. 10018

PRINTED IN U.S.A.

INTRODUCTION

In a unique combination we are presenting on the pages to follow a brand new grading guide and checklist. Now it will be possible for the collector or dealer to keep an accurate record by grade of the coins he owns. It is of the utmost importance for both to know at all times what coins he has and in what grade. The visual pointers on how to grade the different issues will familiarize the novice with grading techniques, and provide a handy reference to which a seasoned collector or dealer can refer to refresh his memory.

In collecting coins, grade or condition is one of the most important factors in establishing numismatic worth. The value of a particular coin depends heavily upon how much wear and tear it has received. The value of the same coin can vary many dollars from grade to grade. Establishing grade is a difficult task and only the most experienced collector or dealer can do so with any degree of accuracy. Mistakes in grading can be costly. You are urged not to be the final authority unless you are a seasoned collector, and if in doubt, consult with one or more dealers of repute. The grading guide that follows is presented as a *guide only*.

Condition or grade of coins are classified as follows:

(PRF) PROOF—Coins with mirror-like surfaces. Specially struck for numismatic purposes.

(UNC) UNCIRCULATED—New with all coin details sharp and unmarred.

(XF) EXTREMELY FINE—High spots just beginning to show wear. Some mint luster may show.

(VF) VERY FINE—Obvious wear on high spots only. Slight mint luster.

(F) FINE—Circulated, but with little wear. All letters in "LIBERTY" mottoes clear.

(VG) VERY GOOD—All letters and designs less clearly defined.

(G) GOOD—All mottoes and designs will show clearly, although they show considerable wear. Each coin must have a full rim on both obverse and reverse.

(FR) FAIR—Coin showing a heavy degree of wear, but still identifiable as to type and grade. The legends and designs will be partially worn off. Date and mint mark should be legible.

Each issue or type has its features which are prominent in attempting to grade that coin. These features are usually the high points of the relief of the coin that ordinarily wear first. The reader's attention is directed to these high points, and a description of what degree of wear occurs at different stages of grades is then presented. Remember that many variables can affect the degree of wear each coin is subjected to. Grading is also very much a matter of opinion, and as in politics these opinions may differ widely. Certain issues are omitted due to space limitations. These are the TWO-CENT PIECES 1864-1872; THREE CENT PIECE (nickel) 1865-1889; THREE CENT PIECE (Silver) 1855-1873; and THREE DOLLAR GOLD PIECES 1854-1889. Also omitted are most of the early issues in the high denominations (1793-1830's). Most coins of these issues are comparatively rare and therefore very valuable. Grading them is a task for the experts.

HALF CENTS
DRAPED BUST TYPE

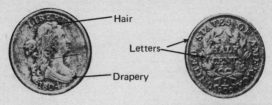

V.F.—Slight wear evident. F.—Drapery and hair worn. V.G.—Faint drapery. G.—No drapery detail. Letters well worn.

CLASSIC HEAD TYPE

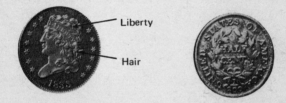

V.F.—Hair finely cut. F.—Liberty and hair on top of head worn. V.G.—Lower curls worn. G.—Liberty only partly visible.

BRAIDED HAIR TYPE

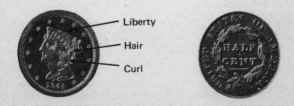

V.F.—Curl shows wear. F.—Hair above ear shows wear. V.G.—Liberty worn. Some hair detail must show. G.—Some of Liberty must show.

LARGE CENTS

Only the obverses are shown as they bear the important grading features.

DRAPED BUST

V.F.—Hair worn but good detail. F.—Hair over brow smooth. V.G.—Drapery worn but still visible. G.—Hair detail gone, lettering worn but legible.

CLASSIC HEAD

V.F.—All hair shows in fine detail. F.—Hair over brow and before ear worn. V.G.—Liberty must be legible. Ear still shows. G.—All hair detail faint. Date very worn.

CORONET TYPE

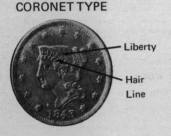

V.F.—Liberty and hair cord in fine detail. F.—Hair and cord worn but still visible. V.G.—Liberty must still be visible and part of cord. G.—All head details well worn.

BRAIDED HAIR

V.F.—Hair above brow in fine detail. F.—Hair at top of head and behind ear shows wear. V.G.—Outline of ear must show. G.—All details worn. Liberty must be legible.

SMALL CENTS
INDIAN HEAD TYPE

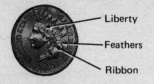

- Liberty
- Feathers
- Ribbon

Ex.F.—Hair ribbon details sharp with some wear at end. Liberty clear. **V.F.**—Ribbon detail partially worn off. Liberty shows wear. **F.**—Liberty shows heavy wear but is complete. **V.G.**—At least half Liberty still visible. **G.**—Liberty will be worn off. Feather detail worn.

LINCOLN CENT (Wheatstalk)

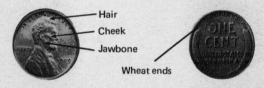

- Hair
- Cheek
- Jawbone
- Wheat ends

Ex.F.—Only wear on hair above ear. **V.F.**—Wear spot on cheek and jawbone. Wheat ends clear. **F.**—Wear at ends of wheat more evident but lines are visible. **V.G.**—Half of lines in wheat ends are visible. **G.**—No detail in wheat ends. Date worn.

NICKELS (Shield Type)

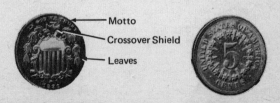

- Motto
- Crossover Shield
- Leaves

Ex.F.—Tips of leaves and cross shows very slight wear. **V.F.**—Heavy wear on olive leaves. **F.**—About half of leaves remain. **V.G.**—All of shield worn but visible. **G.**—Motto very worn but still legible.

NICKELS Cont'd.

LIBERTY HEAD TYPE

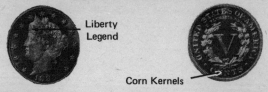

Liberty Legend

Corn Kernels

Ex.F.—Liberty bold. Corn kernels are plain. V.F.—Liberty shows some wear. Corn kernels about half gone. F.—All letters of Liberty must show faintly. V.G.—Three letters of Liberty visible. G.—Head detail rubbed off. Date must still show.

INDIAN HEAD (Buffalo)

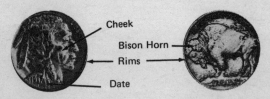

Cheek

Bison Horn

Rims

Date

Ex.F.—Slight wear on all obverse features. Full bison horn. V.F.—Heavy wear on cheekbone. Full horn. F.—Two-thirds of horn must show. Full rims. V.G.—Half of horn visible. Heavy wear on all lettering and date. G.—No horn visible. Date legible.

JEFFERSON

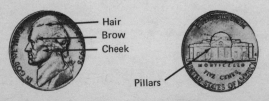

Hair

Brow

Cheek

Pillars

Ex.F.—Wear on cheekbone, hair and eyebrow but all well defined. V.F.—More wear evident. Second porch pillar visible. F.—Cheekbone has flat spot. Eyebrow faint. Second pillar rubbed off at base. V.G.—Second pillar all rubbed off. Others faint.

HALF DIMES

Only the obverses are shown as they bear the important grading features.

CAPPED BUST TYPE

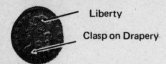

Liberty

Clasp on Drapery

V.F.—Clasp on shoulder drapery clear. F.—All of Liberty shows. V.G.—3 Letters of Liberty must show. Date plain. G.—All bust detail gone. Legend and date legible.

LIBERTY SEATED

Liberty

Legend on Shield

V.F.—All of Liberty well defined. F.—Liberty legible but weak. V.F.—Three letters of Liberty must show. G.—Liberty may be rubbed off shield. Date and legends must be legible.

Coins are enlarged to show better detail

DIMES

The early dimes were of the same design as the half-dimes. The capped bust and seated Liberty types are graded as above.

LIBERTY HEAD (Barber) SERIES

A dime, quarter and half dollar of this period (1892-1915-16) are of the same design the grading for all is very similar.

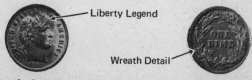

Liberty Legend

Wreath Detail

All wreath details on dime reverse wear evenly.
Coins are enlarged to show better detail

BARBER SERIES Cont'd.

QUARTER AND HALF DOLLAR

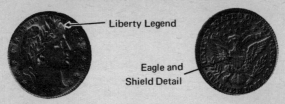

Liberty Legend

Eagle and
Shield Detail

Ex.F.—Liberty clear with ribbon in fine detail. **V.F.**—Some wear on Liberty reverse bold. **F.**—Liberty well worn but all letters legible. **V.G.**—At least 3 letters must be present in Liberty. **G.**—Liberty rubbed off. Date and all legends must be legible.

DIMES Cont'd.

MERCURY TYPE

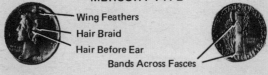

Wing Feathers
Hair Braid
Hair Before Ear
Bands Across Fasces

Ex.F.—Hair braid and wing feathers are clear. Slight wear on high spots of diagonal bands on fasces. **V.F.**—Wear on wings. Flat spots on fasces. **F.**—Wear on hair braid. Vertical rods of fasces faded. **V.G.**—Bands across fasces gone. **G.**—All detail of fasces gone. Date and letters still must be clear.

ROOSEVELT

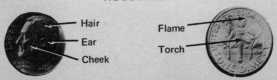

Hair
Ear
Cheek

Flame
Torch

Ex.F.—Hair detail sharp. Ear must be perfect. **V.F.**—Hair above ear shows wear. Base of torch shows wear only. **F.**—Ear detail worn off. Torch detail faded.
Coins are enlarged to show better detail

QUARTERS
CAPPED BUST TYPE

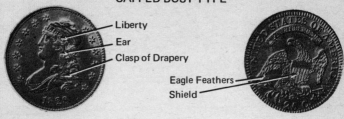

Ex.F.—All details sharp. V.F.—Wear evident but clasp and ear must be clear. F.—Some hair details visible. Ear and clasp still appear. V.G.—Liberty must still be clear. G.—Hair details smooth. All letters and date legible.

SEATED LIBERTY

Only the obverse is shown as it bears important grading features. Ex.F.—Liberty must be sharp. V.F.—Liberty worn but still well defined. F.—Liberty very weak. V.G.—At least 3 letters of Liberty are visible. G.—Liberty gone, rim weak.

LIBERTY HEAD or BARBER QUARTER covered on preceeding pages.

STANDING LIBERTY

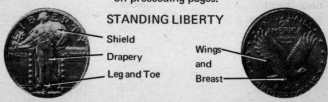

Ex.F.—Figure bold including toes and drapery across right leg. V.F.—Wear evident at top of shield, lower right leg and toe. F.—Drapery visible only along right leg, not over the thigh. V.G.—Toes of right leg must show faintly. Wear on eagle feathers and breast. G.—Right leg rubbed off. Only faint drapery outline. Date shows heavy wear.

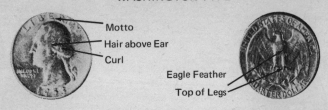

Motto

Hair above Ear

Curl

Eagle Feather

Top of Legs

Ex.F.—Wear evident only at top of eagle's legs. V.F.—Some loss of hair detail. F.—Some detail must remain of eagle breast feathers and hair of Washington V.G.—Top of motto worn. G.—Rims must be fully plain.

HALF DOLLAR
CAPPED BUST

Liberty

Hair Curl

Clasp at Shoulder

Ex.F.—Clasp and all curls bold. V.F.—Curls show heavy wear. F.—Clasp shows heavy wear but still defined. V.G.—Liberty must still be legible. G.—All hair details smooth, date legible. (After 1836 coin was changed and Liberty became high spot. Grade as other capped busts.)

SEATED LIBERTY—QUARTER and HALF DOLLAR
Both denominations are graded the same. "Liberty" in shield is key feature.

Liberty in Shield

Reverse of this coin approx. same as capped bust. Ex.F.—Bold detail to drapery of seated figure. V.F.—Liberty bold. Only wear on ribbon. F.—Liberty whole but faint. V.G.—At least 3 letters of Liberty visible. G.—Liberty gone but date and legends are legible.

HALF DOLLARS

For Liberty Head or "Barber" Half Dollar grading—
see dimes

WALKING LIBERTY

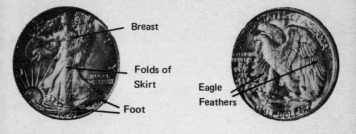

Ex.F.—Fold lines of skirt and toe detail bold. Breast
of Liberty rounded. V.F.—Breast of Liberty flatened.
Eagle feathers show wear. F.—Spots of wear on skirt
folds. Foot below motto clear. V.G.—Skirt lines faded
but must still show. Foot detail rubbed off. G.—
Motto worn but still legible. Date worn but legible.
Rims still defined.

FRANKLIN-LIBERTY BELL

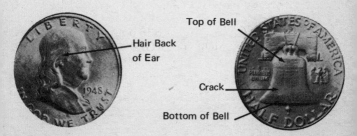

Ex.F.—Wear only at top of curl and back of ear.
Reverse will show slight wear on lines across top of
bell. V.F.—All hair details less clear. Lines at top of
bell partially rubbed off. F.—Wear evident on lines
across bottom of bell. Crack has faded.

SILVER DOLLAR

Early silver dollars 1794-1804 are rare and very valuable. Grading should be attempted by experts only.

For "Liberty Seated" half dollar grading see quarters.

LIBERTY HEAD "MORGAN"

Liberty Motto on Shield

Eagle Feathers

Hairline Detail

Ear

Ex.F.—All obverse details bold. Eagle feathers may show slight wear on breast and wingtips. V.F.—Hairline details from forehead to ear must be partially visible. Center of eagle's breast smooth. F.—Most hair detail gone. All other features show some wear.

PEACE

Hair Detail

Wing Feathers

Ex.F.—Hair detail bold. Some slight wear is evident at top of brow. V.F.—Hair shows wear over eye, but must still be strong over ear. Eagle wings worn all around edges.

GOLD DOLLARS
enlarged 1½ times

Knobs
Liberty
Hair

LIBERTY HEAD 1849-1854

Ex. F.—Knobs on top of coronet must be bold. V.F.—Wear evident on Liberty, hair and knobs, but all complete. F.—Knobs are partially worn. Liberty still complete.

Feathers in
Headress

INDIAN HEAD 1854-1856
(SMALL HEAD)

Ex. F.—Wear only on tips of feather. V.F.—Feather curl visible in outline only. F.—Feather curl only part visible.

Feathers
Hair from
Eye to Ear

INDIAN HEAD 1856-1889
(LARGE HEAD)

Ex. F.—Wear only above eye and top of feather curl. V.F.—Feather curl must have some detail. F.—Feather curl worn off.

QUARTER (2.50) and HALF (5.00) EAGLES

Early types are extremely valuable and should be graded by experts only.

CORONET TYPE
(2.50 and 5.00)

Hair Above
And Below
Coronet

Hair Curl

Ex. F.—Wear only above and below "L" in coronet. V.F.—Hair detail above coronet faded. Hair curl under ear still sharp. F.—Liberty complete. Hair curl has no detail. On reverse of Half-Eagle, motto above the eagle must still be legible.

INCUSE INDIAN HEAD
(2.50 and 5.00)

Feathers
Top of Head
Cheekbone
Knot of
Hair Cord

Ex. F.—Most details extra sharp. Eagle feather on reverse of $5.00 piece will show some wear. V.F.—Knot of haircord must be bold. Wear at cheekbone. Eagle feathers on reverse of $5.00 piece are very worn. F.—Feathers at top of war-bonnet show wear on both. Knot still visible on both.

EAGLES (10.00) GOLD

Early types are extremely valuable and should be graded by experts only.

CORONET TYPE

Hair Above
And Below
Coronet

Motto

Wings and

Neck

Ex.F.—Slight wear top of head and below "L" in Liberty. V.F.—Some outline of hair above coronet must be visible. Motto on reverse is bold. Wings and neck of eagle worn. F.—All letters of Liberty legible.

INDIAN HEAD

War Bonnet
Feathers

Cheekbone

Ex.F.—Wear evident on cheekbone and feathers. V.F.—Feathers well worn around bonnet band. Hair worn. F.—Feathers outlined. Liberty over brow legible.

DOUBLE EAGLES (20.00) LIBERTY HEAD

Crown

Liberty

Hair
Curl

Ex.F.—Wear appears on prongs along top of crown. V.F.—Wear heavy on crown and hair above ear. F.—Liberty worn but legible.

ST. GAUDENS TYPE

Breast

Drapery

Leg

Ex.F.—Drapery folds across top of breast must be defined. V.F.—Slight wear only on right breast, knee and toe.

HALF CENTS

	Good	V. Good	Fine	V. Fine	Ex. Fine	Unc.	Proof	QUANTITY MINTED

LIBERTY CAP TYPE

DATE	Good	V. Good	Fine	V. Fine	Ex. Fine	Unc.	Proof	QUANTITY MINTED
1793.....................								35,000

DATE	Good	V. Good	Fine	V. Fine	Ex. Fine	Unc.	Proof	QUANTITY MINTED
1794.....................								81,600
1795.....................								134,600
1796.....................								6,480
1797.....................								119,215

DRAPED BUST TYPE

DATE	Good	V. Good	Fine	V. Fine	Ex. Fine	Unc.	Proof	QUANTITY MINTED
1800.....................								211,530
1802.....................								14,366
1803.....................								97,900
1804.....................								1,055,312
1805.....................								814,464
1806.....................								356,000
1807.....................								476,000
1808.....................								400,000

TURBAN HEAD TYPE

HALF CENTS

	Good	V. Good	Fine	V. Fine	Ex. Fine	Unc.	Proof	QUANTITY MINTED
1809								1,154,572
1810								215,000
1811								63,140
1825								63,000
1826								234,000
1828								606,000
1829								487,000
1831								2,200
1832								154,000
1833								120,000
1834								141,000
1835								398,000
1836 to 1849								Proof Only

BRAIDED HAIR TYPE

	Good	V. Good	Fine	V. Fine	Ex. Fine	Unc.	Proof	QUANTITY MINTED
1849								39,864
1850								39,812
1851								147,672
1852								Proof Only
1853								129,694
1854								55,358
1855								56,500
1856								40,430
1857								35,180

LARGE CENTS   FLOWING HAIR TYPE

	Good	V. Good	Fine	V. Fine	Ex. Fine	Unc.	Proof	QUANTITY MINTED
1793 Chain AMERI								36,103
1793 Chain AMERICA								

LARGE CENTS

DATE

	Good	V. Good	Fine	V. Fine	Ex. Fine	Unc.	Proof	QUANTITY MINTED

	Good	V. Good	Fine	V. Fine	Ex. Fine	Unc.	Proof	QUANTITY MINTED
1793 Wreath Type......								63,350
1793 Liberty Cap.......								11,056

LIBERTY CAP TYPE

	Good	V. Good	Fine	V. Fine	Ex. Fine	Unc.	Proof	QUANTITY MINTED
1794......................								918,521
1795......................								538,500
1796......................								109,825

DRAPED BUST TYPE

	Good	V. Good	Fine	V. Fine	Ex. Fine	Unc.	Proof	QUANTITY MINTED
1796......................								363,375
1797......................								897,510
1798......................								979,700
1799......................								904,585
1800......................								2,822,175
1801......................								1,362,837
1802......................								3,435,100
1803......................								2,471,353
1804......................								756,838
1805......................								941,116
1806......................								348,000
1807......................								727,221

LARGE CENTS

DATE

	Good	V. Good	Fine	V. Fine	Ex. Fine	Unc.	Proof	QUANTITY MINTED

TURBAN HEAD TYPE

DATE	Good	V. Good	Fine	V. Fine	Ex. Fine	Unc.	Proof	QUANTITY MINTED
1808								1,109,000
1809								222,867
1810								1,458,500
1811								218,025
1812								1,075,500
1813								418,000
1814								357,830

CORONET TYPE

DATE	Good	V. Good	Fine	V. Fine	Ex. Fine	Unc.	Proof	QUANTITY MINTED
1816								2,820,982
1817								3,948,400
1818								3,167,000
1819								2,671,000
1820								4,407,550
1821								389,000
1822								2,072,339
1823								855,730
1824								1,262,000
1825								1,461,100
1826								1,517,425
1827								2,357,732
1828								2,260,624
1829								1,414,500
1830								1,711,500
1831								3,359,260
1832								2,362,000
1833								2,739,000
1834								1,855,100
1835								3,878,400
1836								2,111,000
1837								5,558,300
1838								6,370,200
1839								3,128,661

LARGE CENTS

DATE

	Good	V. Good	Fine	V. Fine	Ex. Fine	Unc.	Proof	QUANTITY MINTED

BRAIDED HAIR TYPE

DATE	Good	V. Good	Fine	V. Fine	Ex. Fine	Unc.	Proof	QUANTITY MINTED
1840								2,462,700
1841								1,597,367
1842								2,383,390
1843								2,428,320
1844								2,398,752
1845								3,894,804
1846								4,120,800
1847								6,183,669
1848								6,415,799
1849								4,178,500
1850								4,426,844
1851								9,889,707
1852								5,063,094
1853								6,641,131
1854								4,236,156
1855								1,574,829
1856								2,690,463
1857								333,456

SMALL CENTS

FLYING EAGLE CENTS

DATE								QUANTITY MINTED
1856								1,000
1857								17,450,000
1858								24,600,000

INDIAN HEAD CENTS
COPPER-NICKEL

SMALL CENTS

DATE	Good	V. Good	Fine	V. Fine	Ex. Fine	Unc.	Proof	QUANTITY MINTED
1859								36,400,000
1860								20,566,000
1861								10,100,000
1862								28,075,000
1863								49,840,000
1864								13,740,000

BRONZE

DATE	Good	V. Good	Fine	V. Fine	Ex. Fine	Unc.	Proof	QUANTITY MINTED
1864 {No L on ribbon								39,233,714
1864L {L on ribbon								35,429,286
1865								35,429,286
1866								9,826,500
1867								9,821,000
1868								10,266,500
1869								6,420,000
1870								5,275,000
1871								3,929,500
1872								4,042,000
1873								11,676,500
1874								14,187,500
1875								13,528,000
1876								7,944,000
1877								852,500
1878								5,799,850
1879								16,231,200
1880								38,964,955
1881								39,211,575
1882								38,581,100
1883								45,598,109
1884								23,261,742
1885								11,765,384
1886								17,654,290
1887								45,226,483
1888								37,494,414
1889								48,869,361
1890								57,182,854
1891								47,072,350
1892								37,649,832
1893								46,642,195
1894								16,752,132
1895								38,343,636
1896								39,057,293
1897								50,466,330

SMALL CENTS

DATE	Good	V. Good	Fine	V. Fine	Ex. Fine	Unc.	Proof	QUANTITY MINTED
1898								49,823,079
1899								53,600,031
1900								66,833,764
1901								79,611,143
1902								87,376,722
1903								85,094,493
1904								61,328,015
1905								80,719,163
1906								96,022,255
1907								108,138,618
1908								32,327,987
1908S								1,115,000
1909								14,370,645
1909S								309,000

LINCOLN HEAD CENTS

	Good	V. Good	Fine	V. Fine	Ex. Fine	Unc.	Proof	QUANTITY MINTED
1909								72,702,618
1909 VDB								27,995,000
1909S								1,825,000
1909S VDB								484,000
1910								146,801,218
1910S								6,045,000
1911								101,177,787
1911D								12,672,000
1911S								4,026,000
1912								68,153,060
1912D								10,411,000
1912S								4,431,000
1913								76,532,352
1913D								15,804,000
1913S								6,101,000
1914								75,238,432
1914D								1,193,000
1914S								4,137,000
1915								29,092,120
1915D								22,050,000
1915S								4,833,000
1916								131,833,677
1916D								35,956,000
1916S								22,510,000
1917								196,429,785
1917D								55,120,000
1917S								32,620,000
1918								288,104,634
1918D								47,830,000

SMALL CENTS

DATE	Good	V. Good	Fine	V. Fine	Ex. Fine	Unc.	Proof	QUANTITY MINTED
1918S.............								34,680,000
1919.................								392,021,000
1919D.............								57,154,000
1919 S............								139,760,000
1920.................								310,165,000
1920D.............								49,280,000
1920 S.............								46,220,000
1921.................								39,157,000
1921 S............								15,274,000
1922 mistrike ...⎫ 1922D...........⎭								7,160,000
1923.................								74,723,000
1923 S.............								8,700,000
1924.................								75,178,000
1924D.............								2,520,000
1924 S.............								11,696,000
1925.................								139,949,000
1925D.............								22,580,000
1925 S.............								26,380,000
1926.................								157,088,000
1926D.............								28,020,000
1926 S.............								4,550,000
1927.................								144,440,000
1927D.............								27,170,000
1927S.............								14,276,000
1928.................								134,116,000
1928D.............								31,170,000
1928S.............								17,266,000
1929.................								185,262,000
1929D.............								41,730,000
1929 S.............								50,148,000
1930.................								157,415,000
1930D.............								40,100,000
1930 S.............								24,286,000
1931.................								19,396,000
1931D.............								4,480,000
1931S.............								866,000
1932.................								9,062,000
1932D.............								10,500,000
1933.................								14,360,000
1933D.............								6,200,000
1934.................								219,080,000
1934D.............								28,446,000
1935.................								245,388,000
1935D.............								47,000,000
1935S.............								38,702,000
1936.................								309,637,569
1936D.............								40,620,000
1936S.............								29,130,000
1937.................								309,179,320
1937D.............								50,430,000

SMALL CENTS

DATE	Good	V. Good	Fine	V. Fine	Ex. Fine	Unc.	Proof	QUANTITY MINTED
1937S								34,500,000
1938								156,696,734
1938D								20,010,000
1938S								15,180,000
1939								316,479,520
1939D								15,160,000
1939S								52,070,000
1940								586,825,872
1940D								81,390,000
1940S								112,940,000
1941								887,039,100
1941D								128,700,000
1941S								92,360,000
1942								657,828,600
1942D								206,698,000
1942S								85,590,000
1943								684,628,670
1943D								217,660,000
1943S								191,550,000
1944								1,435,400,000
1944D								430,578,000
1944S								282,760,000
1945								1,040,515,000
1945D								226,268,000
1945S								181,770,000
1946								991,655,000
1946D								315,690,000
1946S								198,100,000
1947								190,555,000
1947D								194,750,000
1947S								99,000,000
1948								317,570,000
1948D								172,637,500
1948S								81,735,000
1949								217,775,000
1949D								153,132,500
1949S								64,290,000
1950								272,686,386
1950D								334,950,000
1950S								118,505,000
1951								294,633,500
1951D								625,355,000
1951S								136,010,000
1952								186,856,980
1952D								746,130,000
1952S								137,800,004
1953								256,883,800
1953D								700,515,000
1953S								181,835,000
1954								71,873,350
1954D								251,552,500

SMALL CENTS

DATE	Good	V. Good	Fine	V. Fine	Ex. Fine	Unc.	Proof	QUANTITY MINTED
1954S								96,190,000
1955								330,958,200
1955 Double Die								
1955D								563,257,500
1955S								44,610,000
1956								421,414,384
1956D								1,098,201,100
1957								283,787,952
1957D								1,051,342,000
1958								253,400,652
1958D								800,953,300

LINCOLN MEMORIAL TYPE REVERSE

DATE	Good	V. Good	Fine	V. Fine	Ex. Fine	Unc.	Proof	QUANTITY MINTED
1959								610,864,291
1959D								1,279,760,000
1960 Large Date								588,096,602
1960 Small Date								
1960D Large Date								1,580,884,000
1960D Small Date								
1961								756,373,244
1961D								1,753,266,700
1962								609,263,019
1962D								1,793,148,400
1963								757,185,645
1963D								1,774,020,400
1964								2,652,525,762
1964D								3,799,071,500
1965								1,497,224,900
1966								2,188,147,783
1967								3,048,667,100
1968								1,707,880,970
1968D								2,886,269,600
1968S								261,311,570
1969								1,136,910,000
1969D								4,002,382,000
1969S								547,309,631
1970,								
1970D								
1970S,								
1971,								
1971D,								
1971S								

TWO CENTS

TWO CENTS

DATE	Good	V. Good	Fine	V. Fine	Ex. Fine	Unc.	Proof	QUANTITY MINTED
1864 Small Motto								19,847,500
1864								

TWO CENTS

DATE	Good	V. Good	Fine	V. Fine	Ex. Fine	Unc.	Proof	QUANTITY MINTED
1865								13,640,000
1866								3,177,000
1867								2,938,750
1868								2,803,750
1869								1,546,500
1870								861,250
1871								721,250
1872								65,000

THREE CENTS

SILVER THREE-CENT PIECES

DATE	Good	V. Good	Fine	V. Fine	Ex. Fine	Unc.	Proof	QUANTITY MINTED
1851								5,447,400
1851O								720,000
1852								18,663,500
1853								11,400,000
1854								671,000
1855								139,000
1856								1,458,000
1857								1,042,000
1858								1,604,000
1859								365,000
1860								287,000
1861								498,000
1862								343,500
1863								21,460
1864								12,470
1865								8,500
1866								22,725
1867								4,625
1868								4,100
1869								5,100
1870								4,000
1871								4,360
1872								1,950
1873								600

NICKEL THREE-CENT PIECES

DATE	Good	V. Good	Fine	V. Fine	Ex. Fine	Unc.	Proof	QUANTITY MINTED
1865								11,382,000
1866								4,801,000
1867								3,915,000
1868								3,252,000

THREE CENTS

DATE	Good	V. Good	Fine	V. Fine	Ex. Fine	Unc.	Proof	QUANTITY MINTED
1869								1,604,000
1870								1,335,000
1871								604,000
1872								862,000
1873								1,173,000
1874								790,000
1875								228,000
1876								162,000
1877								Proof Only
1878								2,350
1879								41,200
1880								24,955
1881								1,080,575
1882								25,300
1883								10,609
1884								5,642
1885								4,790
1886								4,290
1887								7,961
1888								41,083
1889								21,561

FIVE CENTS

NICKEL FIVE-CENT PIECES
SHIELD TYPE

DATE	Good	V. Good	Fine	V. Fine	Ex. Fine	Unc.	Proof	QUANTITY MINTED
1866 w/rays								14,742,500
1867 w/rays / 1867 no rays								30,909,500
1868								28,817,000
1869								16,395,000
1870								4,806,000
1871								561,000
1872								6,036,000
1873								4,550,000
1874								3,538,000
1875								2,097,000
1876								2,530,000
1877								500
1878								2,350
1879								29,100
1880								19,955
1881								72,375
1882								11,476,600
1883								1,456,919

FIVE CENTS

DATE

	Good	V. Good	Fine	V. Fine	Ex. Fine	Unc.	Proof	QUANTITY MINTED

LIBERTY HEAD TYPE

DATE	Good	V. Good	Fine	V. Fine	Ex. Fine	Unc.	Proof	QUANTITY MINTED
1883 Without Cents								5,479,519
1883 with cents								16,032,983
1884.........................								11,273,942
1885.........................								1,476,490
1886.........................								3,330,290
1887.........................								15,263,652
1888.........................								10,720,483
1889.........................								15,881,361
1890.........................								16,259,272
1891.........................								16,834,350
1892.........................								11,699,642
1893.........................								13,370,195
1894.........................								5,413,132
1895.........................								9,979,884
1896.........................								8,842,920
1897.........................								20,428,735
1898.........................								12,532,087
1899.........................								26,029,031
1900.........................								27,255,995
1901.........................								26,480,213
1902.........................								31,480,579
1903.........................								28,006,725
1904.........................								21,404,984
1905.........................								29,827,276
1906.........................								38,613,725
1907.........................								39,214,800
1908.........................								22,686,177
1909.........................								11,590,526
1910.........................								30,169,353
1911.........................								39,559,372
1912.........................								26,236,714
1912D........................								8,474,000
1912S								238,000

INDIAN HEAD OR BUFFALO TYPE

FIVE CENTS

DATE	Good	V. Good	Fine	V. Fine	Ex. Fine	Unc.	Proof	QUANTITY MINTED
1913 Bison on Mound								30,993,520
1913D Bison on Mound								5,337,000
1913S Bison on Mound								2,105,000
1913 Bison on Flat								29,858,700
1913D Bison on Flat								4,156,000
1913S Bison on Flat								1,209,000
1914........................								20,665,738
1914D......................								3,912,000
1914S								3,470,000
1915........................								20,987,270
1915D......................								7,569,500
1915S								1,505,000
1916........................								63,498,066
1916D......................								13,333,000
1916S								11,860,000
1917........................								51,424,029
1917D......................								9,910,800
1917S								4,193,000
1918........................								32,086,314
1918D......................								8,362,000
1918S								4,882,000
1919........................								60,868,000
1919D......................								8,006,000
1919S								7,521,000
1920........................								63,093,000
1920D......................								9,418,000
1920S								9,689,000
1921........................								10,663,000
1921S								1,557,000
1923........................								35,715,000
1923S								6,142,000
1924........................								21,620,000
1924D......................								5,258,000
1924S								1,437,000
1925........................								35,565,100
1925D......................								4,450,000
1925S								6,256,000
1926........................								44,693,000
1926D......................								5,638,000
1926S								970,000
1927........................								37,981,000
1927D......................								5,730,000
1927S								3,430,000
1928........................								23,411,000
1928D......................								6,436,000
1928S								6,936,000
1929........................								36,446,000
1929D......................								8,370,000
1929S								7,754,000
1930........................								22,849,000
1930S								5,435,000

FIVE CENTS

DATE	Good	V. Good	Fine	V. Fine	Ex. Fine	Unc.	Proof	QUANTITY MINTED
1931S								1,200,000
1934								20,213,000
1934D								7,480,000
1935								58,264,000
1935D								12,092,000
1935S								10,300,000
1936								119,001,420
1936D								24,418,000
1936S								14,930,000
1937								79,485,769
1937D								17,826,000
1937D Three Legged								
1937S								5,635,000
1938D								7,020,000
1938 D over S								

JEFFERSON TYPE

DATE	Good	V. Good	Fine	V. Fine	Ex. Fine	Unc.	Proof	QUANTITY MINTED
1938								19,515,365
1938D								5,376,000
1938S								4,105,000
1939								120,627,535
1939D								3,514,000
1939S								6,630,000
1940								176,499,158
1940D								43,540,000
1940S								39,690,000
1941								203,283,720
1941D								53,432,000
1941S								43,445,000
1942								49,818,600
1942D								13,938,000

WARTIME SILVER — FIVE-CENT PIECES

DATE	Good	V. Good	Fine	V. Fine	Ex. Fine	Unc.	Proof	QUANTITY MINTED
1942P								57,900,600
1942S								32,900,000
1943P								271,165,000
1943D								15,294,000
1943S								104,060,000
1944P								119,150,000
1944D								32,309,000
1944S								21,640,000
1945P								119,408,100
1945D								37,158,000
1945S								58,939,000

FIVE CENTS

	Good	V. Good	Fine	V. Fine	Ex. Fine	Unc.	Proof	QUANTITY MINTED

DATE

REGULAR COMPOSITION — COPPER-NICKEL

DATE	Good	V. Good	Fine	V. Fine	Ex. Fine	Unc.	Proof	QUANTITY MINTED
1946								161,116,000
1946D								45,292,200
1946S								13,560,000
1947								95,000,000
1947D								37,882,000
1947S								24,720,000
1948								89,348,000
1948D								44,734,000
1948S								11,300,000
1949								60,652,000
1949D								36,498,000
1949S								9,716,000
1950								9,847,386
1950D								2,630,030
1951								28,689,500
1951D								20,460,000
1951S								7,776,000
1952								64,069,980
1952D								30,638,000
1952S								20,572,000
1953								46,772,800
1953D								59,878,600
1953S								19,210,900
1954								47,917,350
1954D								117,183,060
1954S								29,384,000
1955								8,266,200
1955D								74,464,100
1956								35,885,384
1956D								67,222,940
1957								39,655,952
1957D								136,828,900
1958								17,963,652
1958D								168,249,120
1959								28,397,291
1959D								160,738,240
1960								57,107,602
1960D								192,582,180
1961								76,668,244
1961D								229,342,760
1962								100,602,019
1962D								280,195,720
1963								178,851,645
1963D								276,829,460
1964								1,028,622,762
1964D								1,787,297,160
1965								136,131,380
1966								156,208,283
1967								107,325,800

FIVE CENTS

DATE	Good	V. Good	Fine	V. Fine	Ex. Fine	Unc.	Proof	QUANTITY MINTED
1968D								91,227,880
1968S								103,437,510
1969D								202,807,500
1969S								123,099,631
1970D								
1970S								
1971D								
1971S								

HALF DIMES

	Good	V. Good	Fine	V. Fine	Ex. Fine	Unc.	Proof	QUANTITY MINTED
1794 } 1795 }								86,416

DRAPED BUST TYPE

	Good	V. Good	Fine	V. Fine	Ex. Fine	Unc.	Proof	QUANTITY MINTED
1796								10,230
1797								44,527

HERALDIC EAGLE TYPE

	Good	V. Good	Fine	V. Fine	Ex. Fine	Unc.	Proof	QUANTITY MINTED
1800								24,000
1801								33,910
1802								13,010
1803								37,850
1805								15,600

LIBERTY CAP TYPE

	Good	V. Good	Fine	V. Fine	Ex. Fine	Unc.	Proof	QUANTITY MINTED
1829								1,230,000
1830								1,240,000
1831								1,242,700
1832								965,000
1833								1,370,000
1834								1,480,000

HALF DIMES

	Good	V. Good	Fine	V. Fine	Ex. Fine	Unc.	Proof	QUANTITY MINTED
1835....................								2,760,000
1836....................								1,900,000
1837....................								2,276,000

LIBERTY SEATED TYPE

NO STARS

	Good	V. Good	Fine	V. Fine	Ex. Fine	Unc.	Proof	QUANTITY MINTED
1837....................								2,276,000
1838O...................								70,000

WITH STARS

	Good	V. Good	Fine	V. Fine	Ex. Fine	Unc.	Proof	QUANTITY MINTED
1838....................								2,255,000
1839....................								1,069,150
1839O...................								1,034,039
1840....................								1,344,085
1840O...................								935,000
1841....................								1,150,000
1841O...................								815,000
1842....................								815,000
1842O...................								350,000
1843....................								1,165,000
1844....................								430,000
1844O...................								220,000
1845....................								1,564,000
1846....................								27,000
1847....................								1,274,000
1848....................								668,000
1848O...................								600,000
1849....................								1,309,000
1849O...................								140,000
1850....................								955,000
1850O...................								690,000
1851....................								781,000
1851O...................								860,000
1852....................								1,000,500
1852O...................								260,000
1853....................								135,000
1853 Arrows at Date								13,210,020
1853O No Arrows								160,000
1853O Arrows								2,200,000
1854 Arrows...........								5,740,000
1854O Arrows..........								1,560,000
1855 Arrows...........								1,750,000
1855O Arrows..........								600,000
1856 No Arrows								4,880,000
1856O..................								1,100,000

HALF DIMES

DATE	Good	V. Good	Fine	V. Fine	Ex. Fine	Unc.	Proof	QUANTITY MINTED
1857								7,280,000
1857O								1,380,000
1858								3,500,000
1858O								1,660,000
1859								340,000
1859O								560,000

LEGEND REPLACES STARS

DATE	Good	V. Good	Fine	V. Fine	Ex. Fine	Unc.	Proof	QUANTITY MINTED
1860								799,000
1860O								1,060,000
1861								3,361,000
1862								1,492,550
1863								18,460
1863S								100,000
1864								48,470
1864S								90,000
1865								13,500
1865S								120,000
1866								10,725
1866S								120,000
1867								8,625
1867S								120,000
1868								89,200
1868S								280,000
1869								208,600
1869S								230,000
1870								536,600
1871								1,873,960
1871S								161,000
1872								2,947,950
1872S								837,000
1873								712,600
1873S								324,000

DIMES

DRAPED BUST TYPE

DATE	Good	V. Good	Fine	V. Fine	Ex. Fine	Unc.	Proof	QUANTITY MINTED
1796								22,135
1797								25,261

DIMES

DATE

	Good	V. Good	Fine	V. Fine	Ex. Fine	Unc.	Proof	QUANTITY MINTED

HERALDIC EAGLE TYPE

DATE	Good	V. Good	Fine	V. Fine	Ex. Fine	Unc.	Proof	QUANTITY MINTED
1798								27,550
1800								21,760
1801								34,640
1802								10,975
1803								33,040
1804								8,265
1805								120,780
1807								165,000

LIBERTY CAP TYPE

DATE	Good	V. Good	Fine	V. Fine	Ex. Fine	Unc.	Proof	QUANTITY MINTED
1809								44,710
1811								65,180
1814								421,500
1820								942,587
1821								1,186,512
1822								100,000
1823								440,000
1824								
1825								510,000
1827								1,215,000
1828								125,000
1829								770,000
1830								510,000
1831								771,350
1832								522,500
1833								485,000
1834								635,000
1835								1,410,000
1836								1,190,000
1837								1,042,000

LIBERTY SEATED TYPE

DIMES

DATE	Good	V. Good	Fine	V. Fine	Ex. Fine	Unc.	Proof	QUANTITY MINTED
No Stars on Obverse								
1837........................								
1838O........................								406,034
With Stars on Obverse								
1838........................								1,992,500
1839........................								1,053,115
1839O........................								1,323,000
1840........................								1,358,580
1840O........................								1,175,000
1841........................								1,622,500
1841O........................								2,007,500
1842........................								1,887,500
1842O........................								2,020,000
1843........................								1,370,000
1843O........................								150,000
1844........................								72,500
1845........................								1,755,000
1845O........................								230,000
1846........................								31,300
1847........................								245,000
1848........................					.			451,500
1849........................								839,000
1849O........................								300,000
1850........................								1,931,500
1850O........................								510,000
1851........................								1,026,500
1851O........................								400,000
1852........................								1,535,500
1852O........................								430,000
1853 No Arrows								95,000
1853 Arrows at Date								12,173,010
1853O........................								1,100,000
1854								4,470,000
1854O........................								1,770,000
1855								2,075,000
1856........................								5,780,000
1856O........................								1,180,000
1856S........................								70,000
1857........................								5,580,000
1857O........................								1,540,000
1858........................								1,540,000
1858O........................								290,000
1858S........................								60,000
1859........................								430,000
1859O........................								480,000
1859S........................								60,000
1860S........................								140,000

DIMES

DATE

	Good	V. Good	Fine	V. Fine	Ex. Fine	Unc.	Proof	QUANTITY MINTED

LEGEND REPLACES STARS ON OBVERSE

DATE	Good	V. Good	Fine	V. Fine	Ex. Fine	Unc.	Proof	QUANTITY MINTED
1860								607,000
1860O								40,000
1861								1,884,000
1861S								172,500
1862								847,550
1862S								180,750
1863								14,460
1863S								157,500
1864								11,470
1864S								230,000
1865								10,500
1865S								175,000
1866								8,725
1866S								135,000
1867								6,625
1867S								140,000
1868								464,600
1868S								260,000
1869								256,600
1869S								450,000
1870								471,500
1870S								50,000
1871								907,710
1871CC								20,100
1871S								320,000
1872								2,396,450
1872CC								24,000
1872S								190,000
1873								1,568,600
1873 Arrows at Date								2,378,500
1873CC No Arrows								12,400
1873CC Arrows								18,791
1873S Arrows								455,000
1874 Arrows								2,940,700
1874CC Arrows								10,817
1874S Arrows								240,000
1875 No Arrows								10,350,700
1875CC								4,645,000
1875S								9,070,000
1876								11,461,150
1876CC								8,270,000
1876S								10,420,000
1877								7,310,510

DIMES

DATE	Good	V. Good	Fine	V. Fine	Ex. Fine	Unc.	Proof	QUANTITY MINTED
1877CC................								7,700,000
1877S.................								2,340,000
1878.................								1,678,800
1878CC..............								200,000
1879.................								15,100
1880.................								37,355
1881.................								24,975
1882.................								3,911,100
1883.................								7,675,712
1884.................								3,366,380
1884S................								564,969
1885.................								2,533,427
1885S................								43,690
1886.................								6,377,570
1886S................								206,524
1887.................								11,283,939
1887S................								4,454,450
1888.................								5,496,487
1888S................								1,720,000
1889.................								7,380,711
1889S................								972,678
1890.................								9,911,541
1890S................								1,423,076
1891.................								15,310,600
1891O................								4,540,000
1891S................								3,196,116

LIBERTY HEAD OR BARBER TYPE

DATE	Good	V. Good	Fine	V. Fine	Ex. Fine	Unc.	Proof	QUANTITY MINTED
1892.................								12,121,245
1892O................								3,841,700
1892S................								990,710
1893.................								3,340,792
1893O................								1,760,000
1893S................								2,491,401
1894.................								1,330,972
1894O................								720,000
1894S................								24
1895.................								690,880
1895O................								440,000
1895S................								1,120,000
1896.................								2,000,762
1896O................								610,000
1896S................								575,056
1897.................								10,869,264
1897O................								666,000

DIMES

DATE	Good	V. Good	Fine	V. Fine	Ex. Fine	Unc.	Proof	QUANTITY MINTED
1897S								1,342,844
1898								16,320,735
1898O								2,130,000
1898S								1,702,507
1899								19,580,846
1899O								2,650,000
1899S								1,867,493
1900								17,600,912
1900O								2,010,000
1900S								5,168,270
1901								18,860,478
1901O								5,620,000
1901S								593,022
1902								21,380,777
1902O								4,500,000
1902S								2,070,000
1903								19,500,755
1903O								8,180,000
1903S								613,300
1904								14,601,027
1904S								800,000
1905								14,552,350
1905O								3,400,000
1905S								6,855,199
1906								19,958,406
1906D								4,060,000
1906O								2,610,000
1906S								3,136,640
1907								22,220,575
1907D								4,080,000
1907O								5,058,000
1907S								3,178,470
1908								10,600,545
1908D								7,490,000
1908O								1,789,000
1908S								3,220,000
1909								10,240,650
1909D								954,000
1909O								2,287,000
1909S								1,000,000
1910								11,520,551
1910D								3,490,000
1910S								1,240,000
1911								18,870,543
1911D								11,209,000
1911S								3,520,000
1912								19,350,700
1912D								11,760,000
1912S								3,420,000
1913								19,760,622
1913S								510,000

DIMES

DATE	Good	V. Good	Fine	V. Fine	Ex. Fine	Unc.	Proof	QUANTITY MINTED
1914......................								17,360,655
1914D.....................								11,908,000
1914S								2,100,000
1915......................								5,620,450
1915S								960,000
1916......................								18,490,000
1916S								5,820,000

WINGED HEAD OF LIBERTY OR "MERCURY" TYPE

DATE	Good	V. Good	Fine	V. Fine	Ex. Fine	Unc.	Proof	QUANTITY MINTED
1916......................								22,180,080
1916D.....................								264,000
1916S								10,450,000
1917......................								55,230,000
1917D.....................								9,402,000
1917S								27,330,000
1918......................								26,680,000
1918D.....................								22,674,800
1918S								19,300,000
1919......................								35,740,000
1919D.....................								9,939,000
1919S								8,850,000
1920......................								59,030,000
1920D.....................								19,171,000
1920S								13,820,000
1921......................								1,230,000
1921D.....................								1,080,000
1923......................								50,130,000
1923S								6,440,000
1924......................								24,010,000
1924D.....................								6,810,000
1924S								7,120,000
1925......................								25,610,000
1925D.....................								5,117,000
1925S								5,850,000
1926......................								32,160,000
1926D.....................								6,828,000
1926S								1,520,000
1927......................								28,080,000
1927D.....................								4,812,000
1927S								4,770,000
1928......................								19,480,000
1928D.....................								4,161,000
1928S								7,400,000
1929......................								25,970,000
1929D.....................								5,034,000

DIMES

DATE	Good	V. Good	Fine	V. Fine	Ex. Fine	Unc.	Proof	QUANTITY MINTED
1929S								4,730,000
1930								6,770,000
1930S								1,843,000
1931								3,150,000
1931D								1,260,000
1931S								1,800,000
1934								24,080,000
1934D								6,772,000
1935								58,830,000
1935D								10,477,000
1935S								15,840,000
1936								87,504,130
1936D								16,132,000
1936S								9,210,000
1937								56,865,756
1937D								14,146,000
1937S								9,740,000
1938								22,198,728
1938D								5,537,000
1938S								8,090,000
1939								67,749,321
1939D								24,394,000
1939S								10,540,000
1940								65,361,827
1940D								21,198,000
1940S								21,560,000
1941								175,106,557
1941D								45,634,000
1941S								43,090,000
1942 1942 over 1941								205,432,329
1942D								60,740,000
1942S								49,300,000
1943								191,710,000
1943D								71,949,000
1943S								60,400,000
1944								231,410,000
1944D								62,224,000
1944S								49,490,000
1945								159,130,000
1945D								40,245,000
1945S								41,920,000
1945 Micro S								

ROOSEVELT
TYPE

	Good	V. Good	Fine	V. Fine	Ex. Fine	Unc.	Proof	QUANTITY MINTED
1946								255,250,000
1946D								61,043,500

DIMES

DATE	Good	V. Good	Fine	V. Fine	Ex. Fine	Unc.	Proof	QUANTITY MINTED
1946S								27,900,000
1947								121,520,000
1947D								46,835,000
1947S								34,840,000
1948								74,950,000
1948D								52,841,000
1948S								35,520,000
1949								30,940,000
1949D								26,034,000
1949S								13,510,000
1950								50,181,500
1950D								46,803,000
1950S								20,440,000
1951								103,937,602
1951D								56,529,000
1951S								31,630,000
1952								99,122,073
1952D								122,100,000
1952S								44,419,500
1953								53,618,920
1953D								136,433,000
1953S								39,180,000
1954								114,243,503
1954D								106,397,000
1954S								22,860,000
1955								12,828,381
1955D								13,959,000
1955S								18,510,000
1956								109,309,384
1956D								108,015,100
1957								161,407,952
1957D								113,354,330
1958								32,785,652
1958D								136,564,600
1959								86,929,291
1959D								164,919,790
1960								72,081,602
1960D								200,160,400
1961								96,758,244
1961D								209,146,550
1962								75,668,019
1962D								334,948,380
1963								126,725,645
1963D								421,476,530
1964								933,310,762
1964D								1,357,517,180

CLAD OR SILVERLESS COINS

DATE	Good	V. Good	Fine	V. Fine	Ex. Fine	Unc.	Proof	QUANTITY MINTED
1965								1,652,140,570
1966								1,382,734,540
1967								2,244,007,320
1968								424,470,400

DIMES

DATE	Good	V. Good	Fine	V. Fine	Ex. Fine	Unc.	Proof	QUANTITY MINTED
1968D.................								480,748,280
1968S Proof Only								3,041,509
1969								145,790,000
1969D								563,323,870
1969S Proof Only								2,934,631
1970, ...								
1970D................								
1970S................								
1971, ...								
1971D................								
1971S................								

TWENTY CENTS

DATE	Good	V. Good	Fine	V. Fine	Ex. Fine	Unc.	Proof	QUANTITY MINTED
1875...................								39,700
1875CC................								133,290
1875S.................								1,155,000
1876...................								15,900
1876CC................								10,000
1877...................								510
1878...................								600

QUARTERS

DATE	Good	V. Good	Fine	V. Fine	Ex. Fine	Unc.	Proof	QUANTITY MINTED
1796......................								6,146

DATE	Good	V. Good	Fine	V. Fine	Ex. Fine	Unc.	Proof	QUANTITY MINTED
1804......................								6,738
1805......................								121,394
1806......................								206,124
1807......................								220,643

QUARTERS

DATE

DATE	Good	V. Good	Fine	V. Fine	Ex. Fine	Unc.	Proof	QUANTITY MINTED
1815....................								89,235
1818....................								361,174
1819....................								144,000
1820....................								127,444
1821....................								216,851
1822....................								64,080
1823....................								17,800
1824....................								
1825....................								168,000
1827....................								4,000
1828....................								102,000

DATE	Good	V. Good	Fine	V. Fine	Ex. Fine	Unc.	Proof	QUANTITY MINTED
1831....................								398,000
1832....................								320,000
1833....................								156,000
1834....................								286,000
1835....................								1,952,000
1836....................								472,000
1837....................								252,400
1838 part of								832,000

LIBERTY SEATED TYPE

QUARTERS

DATE	Good	V. Good	Fine	V. Fine	Ex. Fine	Unc.	Proof	QUANTITY MINTED
1838 part of								832,000
1839........................								491,146
1840 drapery,............								188,127
1840O ↓							{	425,200
1840O no drapery								
1841........................								120,000
1841O......................								452,000
1842 sm. date							{	88,000
1842 lg. date								
1842O sm. date							{	769,000
1842O lg. date								
1843........................								645,600
1843O......................								968,000
1844........................								421,200
1844O......................								740,000
1845........................								922,000
1846........................								510,000
1847........................								734,000
1847O......................								368,000
1848........................								146,000
1849........................								340,000
1849O......................								
1850........................								190,800
1850O......................								412,000
1851........................								160,000
1851O......................								88,000
1852........................								177,060
1852O......................								96,000
1853 recut date								44,200

ARROWS AT DATE

	Good	V. Good	Fine	V. Fine	Ex. Fine	Unc.	Proof	QUANTITY MINTED
1853 Rays								15,254,220
1853O Rays								1,332,000
1854 no rays............								12,380,000
1854O....│...............								1,484,000
1855......│...............								2,857,000
1855O....│...............								176,000
1855S....▼..............								396,400

	Good	V. Good	Fine	V. Fine	Ex. Fine	Unc.	Proof	QUANTITY MINTED
1856 No Arrows.........								7,264,000
1856O....│...............								968,000
1856S ....│...............								286,000
1857......│...............								9,644,000
1857O....│...............								1,180,000
1857S ....▼...............								82,000

QUARTERS

DATE	Good	V. Good	Fine	V. Fine	Ex. Fine	Unc.	Proof	QUANTITY MINTED
1858........................								7,368,000
1858O.......................								520,000
1858S.......................								121,000
1859........................								1,344,000
1859O.......................								260,000
1859S.......................								80,000
1860........................								805,400
1860O.......................								388,000
1860S.......................								56,000
1861........................								4,854,600
1861S.......................								96,000
1862........................								932,550
1862S.......................								67,000
1863........................								192,060
1864........................								94,070
1864S.......................								20,000
1865........................								59,300
1865S.......................								41,000

MOTTO ABOVE EAGLE

ARROWS AT DATE 1873-1874

	Good	V. Good	Fine	V. Fine	Ex. Fine	Unc.	Proof	QUANTITY MINTED
1866........................								17,525
1866S.......................								28,000
1867........................								20,625
1867S.......................								48,000
1868........................								30,000
1868S.......................								96,000
1869........................								16,600
1869S.......................								76,000
1870........................								87,400
1870CC.....................								8,340
1871........................								119,160
1871CC.....................								10,890
1871S.......................								30,900
1872........................								182,950
1872CC.....................								9,100
1872S.......................								83,000
1873........................								212,600
1873CC.....................								4,000
1873 Arrows.........								1,271,700
1873CC Arrows.........								12,462
1873S Arrows.........								156,000

QUARTERS

DATE	Good	V. Good	Fine	V. Fine	Ex. Fine	Unc.	Proof	QUANTITY MINTED
1874 Arrows.........								471,900
1874S Arrows.........								392,000
1875....................								4,293,500
1875CC................								140,000
1875S								680,000
1876....................								17,817,150
1876CC................								4,944,000
1876S								8,596,000
1877....................								10,911,710
1877CC................								4,192,000
1877S								8,996,000
1878....................								2,260,800
1878CC................								996,000
1878S								140,000
1879....................								14,700
1880....................								14,955
1881....................								12,975
1882....................								16,300
1883....................								15,439
1884....................								8,875
1885....................								14,530
1886....................								5,886
1887....................								10,710
1888....................								10,833
1888S								1,216,000
1889....................								12,711
1890....................								80,590
1891....................								3,920,600
1891O..................								68,000
1891S								2,216,000

LIBERTY HEAD OR BARBER TYPE

	Good	V. Good	Fine	V. Fine	Ex. Fine	Unc.	Proof	QUANTITY MINTED
1892....................								8,237,245
1892O..................								2,640,000
1892S								964,079
1893....................								5,444,815
1893O..................								3,396,000
1893S								1,454,535
1894....................								3,432,972
1894O..................								2,852,000
1894S								2,648,821
1895....................								4,440,880

QUARTERS

DATE	Good	V. Good	Fine	V. Fine	Ex. Fine	Unc.	Proof	QUANTITY MINTED
1895O								2,816,000
1895S								1,764,681
1896								3,874,762
1896O								1,484,000
1896S								188,039
1897								8,140,731
1897O								1,414,800
1897S								542,229
1898								11,100,735
1898O								1,868,000
1898S								1,020,592
1899								12,624,846
1899O								2,644,000
1899S								708,000
1900								10,016,912
1900O								3,416,000
1900S								1,858,585
1901								8,892,813
1901O								1,612,000
1901S								72,664
1902								12,197,744
1902O								4,748,000
1902S								1,524,612
1903								9,670,064
1903O								3,500,000
1903S								1,036,000
1904								9,588,813
1904O								2,456,000
1905								4,968,250
1905O								1,230,000
1905S								1,884,000
1906								3,656,435
1906D								3,280,000
1906O								2,056,000
1907								7,192,575
1907D								2,484,000
1907O								4,560,000
1907S								1,360,000
1908								4,232,545
1908D								5,788,000
1908O								6,244,000
1908S								784,000
1909								9,268,650
1909D								5,114,000
1909O								712,000
1909S								1,348,000
1910								2,244,551
1910D								1,500,000
1911								3,720,543
1911D								933,600
1911S								988,000

QUARTERS

DATE	Good	V. Good	Fine	V. Fine	Ex. Fine	Unc.	Proof	QUANTITY MINTED
1912								4,400,700
1912S								708,000
1913								484,613
1913D								1,450,800
1913S								40,000
1914								6,244,610
1914D								3,046,000
1914S								264,000
1915								3,480,450
1915D								3,694,000
1915S								704,000
1916								1,788,000
1916D								6,540,800

LIBERTY STANDING TYPE

DATE	Good	V. Good	Fine	V. Fine	Ex. Fine	Unc.	Proof	QUANTITY MINTED
1916								52,000
1917								8,792,000
1917D								1,509,200
1917S								1,952,000

DATE	Good	V. Good	Fine	V. Fine	Ex. Fine	Unc.	Proof	QUANTITY MINTED
1917								13,880,000
1917D								6,224,400
1917S								5,552,000
1918								14,240,000
1918D								7,380,000
1918S								11,072,000
1919								11,324,000
1919D								1,944,000
1919S								1,836,000
1920								27,860,000
1920D								3,586,400
1920S								6,380,000
1921								1,916,000
1923								9,716,000
1923S								1,360,000

QUARTERS

DATE	Good	V. Good	Fine	V. Fine	Ex. Fine	Unc.	Proof	QUANTITY MINTED
1924								10,920,000
1924D								3,112,000
1924S								2,860,000
1925								12,280,000
1926								11,316,000
1926D								1,716,000
1926S								2,700,000
1927								11,912,000
1927D								976,400
1927S								396,000
1928								6,336,000
1928D								1,627,600
1928S								2,644,000
1929								11,140,000
1929D								1,358,000
1929S								1,764,000
1930								5,632,000
1930S								1,556,000

WASHINGTON TYPE

DATE	Good	V. Good	Fine	V. Fine	Ex. Fine	Unc.	Proof	QUANTITY MINTED
1932								5,404,000
1932D								436,800
1932S								408,000
1934								31,912,052
1934D								3,527,200
1935								32,484,000
1935D								5,780,000
1935S								5,660,000
1936								41,303,837
1936D								5,374,000
1936S								3,828,000
1937								19,701,542
1937D								7,189,600
1937S								1,652,000
1938								9,480,045
1938S								2,832,000
1939								33,548,795
1939D								7,092,000
1939S								2,628,000
1940								35,715,246
1940D								2,797,600
1940S								8,244,000
1941								79,047,287

QUARTERS

DATE	Good	V. Good	Fine	V. Fine	Ex. Fine	Unc.	Proof	QUANTITY MINTED
1941D								16,714,800
1941S								16,080,000
1942								102,117,123
1942D								17,487,200
1942S								19,384,000
1943								99,700,000
1943D								16,095,600
1943S								21,700,000
1944								104,956,000
1944D								14,600,800
1944S								12,560,000
1945								74,372,000
1945D								12,341,600
1945S								17,004,001
1946								53,436,000
1946D								9,072,800
1946S								4,204,000
1947								22,556,000
1947D								15,338,400
1947S								5,532,000
1948								35,196,000
1948D								16,766,800
1948S								15,960,000
1949								9,312,000
1949D								10,068,400
1950								24,971,512
1950D								21,075,600
1950S								10,284,004
1951								43,505,602
1951D								35,354,800
1951S								8,948,000
1952								38,862,073
1952D								49,795,200
1952S								13,707,800
1953								18,664,920
1953D								56,112,400
1953S								14,016,000
1954								54,645,503
1954D								46,305,500
1954S								11,834,722
1955								18,558,381
1955D								3,182,400
1956								44,813,384
1956D								32,334,500
1957								47,779,952
1957D								77,924,160
1958								7,235,652
1958D								78,124,900
1959								25,533,291
1959D								62,054,232
1960								30,855,602

QUARTERS

DATE	Good	V. Good	Fine	V. Fine	Ex. Fine	Unc.	Proof	QUANTITY MINTED
1960D								63,000,324
1961								37,036,000
1961D								83,656,928
1962								39,374,019
1962D								127,554,756
1963								77,391,645
1963D								135,288,184
1964								564,341,347
1964D								704,135,528

CLAD OR SILVERLESS COINS

DATE	Good	V. Good	Fine	V. Fine	Ex. Fine	Unc.	Proof	QUANTITY MINTED
1965								1,819,717,540
1966								821,101,500
1967								1,524,031,848
1968								220,731,500
1968D								101,534,000
1968S Proof Only								3,041,509
1969								176,212,000
1969D								114,372,000
1969S Proof Only								2,934,631
1970								
1970D								
1970S Proof Only								
1971								
1971D								
1971S								

HALF DOLLARS

FLOWING HAIR TYPE

DATE	Good	V. Good	Fine	V. Fine	Ex. Fine	Unc.	Proof	QUANTITY MINTED
1794								5,300
1795								317,836

DRAPED BUST

HALF DOLLARS

DATE	Good	V. Good	Fine	V. Fine	Ex. Fine	Unc.	Proof	QUANTITY MINTED
1796 ⎱ 1797 ⎰								3,918

HERALDIC REVERSE

DATE	Good	V. Good	Fine	V. Fine	Ex. Fine	Unc.	Proof	QUANTITY MINTED
1801..........................								30,289
1802..........................								29,890
1803 Sm. 3								31,715
1803 Lg. 3								188,234
1805..........................								211,722
1806..........................								839,576
1807..........................								301,076

TURBAN HEAD TYPE

DATE	Good	V. Good	Fine	V. Fine	Ex. Fine	Unc.	Proof	QUANTITY MINTED
1807..........................								750,500
1808..........................								1,368,600
1809..........................								1,405,810
1810..........................								1,276,276
1811..........................								1,203,644
1812..........................								1,628,059
1813..........................								1,241,903
1814..........................								1,039,075
1815..........................								47,150
1817..........................								1,215,567
1818..........................								1,960,322
1819..........................								2,208,000
1820..........................								751,122
1821..........................								1,305,797
1822..........................								1,559,573
1823..........................								1,694,200
1824..........................								3,504,954
1825..........................								2,943,166
1826..........................								4,004,180
1827..........................								5,493,400

HALF DOLLARS

DATE	Good	V. Good	Fine	V. Fine	Ex. Fine	Unc.	Proof	QUANTITY MINTED
1828								3,075,200
1829								3,712,156
1830								4,764,800
1831								5,873,660
1832								4,797,000
1833								5,206,000
1834								6,412,004
1835								5,352,006
1836								6,546,200

REEDED EDGE 50 CENTS

	Good	V. Good	Fine	V. Fine	Ex. Fine	Unc.	Proof	QUANTITY MINTED
1836								
1837								3,629,820

HALF DOL

	Good	V. Good	Fine	V. Fine	Ex. Fine	Unc.	Proof	QUANTITY MINTED
1838								3,546,000
1838O				very rare				20
1839								3,334,560
1839O								178,976

LIBERTY SEATED TYPE

HALF DOLLARS

DATE	Good	V. Good	Fine	V. Fine	Ex. Fine	Unc.	Proof	QUANTITY MINTED
1839								
1840								1,435,008
1840O								855,100
1841								310,000
1841O								401,000
1842								2,012,764
1842O								957,000
1843								3,844,000
1843O								2,268,000
1844								1,766,000
1844O								2,005,000
1845								589,000
1845O								2,094,000
1846								2,210,000
1846O								2,304,000
1847								1,156,000
1847O								2,584,000
1848								580,000
1848O								3,180,000
1849								1,252,000
1849O								2,310,000
1850								227,000
1850O								2,456,000
1851								200,750
1851O								402,000
1852								77,130
1852O								144,000

DATE	Good	V. Good	Fine	V. Fine	Ex. Fine	Unc.	Proof	QUANTITY MINTED
1853								3,532,708
1853O								1,328,000
1854 Arrows at Date								2,982,000
1854O Arrows								5,240,000
1855								759,500
1855O								3,688,000
1855S								129,950
1856 No Arrows								938,000
1956O								2,658,000
1856S								211,000
1857								1,988,000

HALF DOLLARS

DATE	Good	V. Good	Fine	V. Fine	Ex. Fine	Unc.	Proof	QUANTITY MINTED
1857O								818,000
1857S								158,000
1858								4,226,000
1858O								7,294,000
1858S								476,000
1859								748,000
1859O								2,834,000
1859S								566,000
1860								303,700
1860O								1,290,000
1860S								472,000
1861								2,888,400
1861O								2,532,633
1861S								939,500
1862								253,550
1862S								1,352,000
1863								503,660
1863S								916,000
1864								379,570
1864S								658,000
1865								511,900
1865S								675,000
1866S part of								1,054,C00

MOTTO ABOVE EAGLE

DATE	Good	V. Good	Fine	V. Fine	Ex. Fine	Unc.	Proof	QUANTITY MINTED
1866								745,625
1866S part of								1,054,000
1867								449,925
1867S								1,196,000
1868								418,200
1868S								1,160,000
1869								795,900
1869S								656,000
1870								634,900
1870CC								54,617
1870S								1,004,000
1871								1,204,560
1871CC								139,950
1871S								2,178,000
1872								881,550
1872CC								272,000
1872S								580,000
1873								801,800
1873CC								122,500
1873 Arrows at Date								1,815,700
1873CC Arrows								214,560
1873S Arrows								228,000
1874								2,360,300
1874CC								59,000
1874S								394,000
1875 No Arrows								6,027,500
1875CC								1,008,000

HALF DOLLARS

DATE	Good	V. Good	Fine	V. Fine	Ex. Fine	Unc.	Proof	QUANTITY MINTED
1875S								3,200,000
1876								8,419,150
1876CC								1,956,000
1876S								4,528,000
1877								8,304,510
1877CC								1,420,000
1877S								5,356,000
1878								1,378,400
1878CC								62,000
1878S								12,000
1879								5,900
1880								9,755
1881								10,975
1882								5,500
1883								9,039
1884								5,275
1885								6,130
1886								5,886
1887								5,710
1888								12,833
1889								12,711
1890								12,590
1891								200,600

LIBERTY HEAD OR BARBER TYPE

	Good	V. Good	Fine	V. Fine	Ex. Fine	Unc.	Proof	QUANTITY MINTED
1892								935,245
1892O								390,000
1892S								1,029,028
1893								1,826,792
1893O								1,389,000
1893S								740,000
1894								1,148,972
1894O								2,138,000
1894S								4,048,690
1895								1,835,218
1895O								1,766,000
1895S								1,108,086
1896								950,762
1896O								924,000
1896S								1,140,948
1897								2,480,731
1897O								632,000

HALF DOLLARS

DATE	Good	V. Good	Fine	V. Fine	Ex. Fine	Unc.	Proof	QUANTITY MINTED
1897S								933,900
1898								2,956,735
1898O								874,000
1898S								2,358,550
1899								5,538,846
1899O								1,724,000
1899S								1,686,411
1900								4,762,912
1900O								2,744,000
1900S								2,560,322
1901								4,268,813
1901O								1,124,000
1901S								847,044
1902								4,922,777
1902O								2,526,000
1902S								1,460,670
1903								2,278,755
1903O								2,100,000
1903S								1,920,772
1904								2,992,670
1904O								1,117,600
1904S								553,038
1905								662,727
1905O								505,000
1905S								2,494,000
1906								2,638,675
1906D								4,028,000
1906O								2,446,000
1906S								1,740,154
1907								2,598,575
1907D								3,856,000
1907O								3,946,000
1907S								1,250,000
1908								1,354,545
1908D								3,280,000
1908O								5,360,000
1908S								1,644,828
1909								2,368,650
1909O								925,400
1909S								1,764,000
1910								418,551
1910S								1,948,000
1911								1,406,543
1911D								695,080
1911S								1,272,000
1912								1,550,700
1912D								2,300,800
1912S								1,370,000
1913								188,627
1913D								534,000

HALF DOLLARS

DATE	Good	V. Good	Fine	V. Fine	Ex. Fine	Unc.	Proof	QUANTITY MINTED
1913S								604,000
1914								124,610
1914S								992,000
1915								138,450
1915D								1,170,400
1915S								1,604,000

WALKING LIBERTY TYPE

DATE	Good	V. Good	Fine	V. Fine	Ex. Fine	Unc.	Proof	QUANTITY MINTED
1916								608,000
1916D on Obverse								1,014,400
1916S on Obverse								508,000
1917								12,292,000
1917D on Obverse								765,400
1917D on reverse								1,940,000
1917S on Obverse								952,000
1917S on reverse								5,554,000
1918								6,634,000
1918D								3,853,040
1918S								10,282,000
1919								962,000
1919D								1,165,000
1919S								1,552,000
1920								6,372,000
1920D								1,551,000
1920S								4,624,000
1921								246,000
1921D								208,000
1921S								548,000
1923S								2,178,000
1927S								2,392,000
1928S								1,940,000
1929D								1,001,200
1929S								1,902,000
1933S								1,786,000
1934								6,964,000
1934D								2,361,400
1934S								3,652,000
1935								9,162,000
1935D								3,003,800
1935S								3,854,000
1936								12,617,901

HALF DOLLARS

DATE	Good	V. Good	Fine	V. Fine	Ex. Fine	Unc.	Proof	QUANTITY MINTED
1936D								4,252,400
1936S								3,884,000
1937								9,527,728
1937D								1,760,001
1937S								2,090,000
1938								4,118,152
1938D								491,600
1939								6,820,808
1939D								4,267,800
1939S								2,552,000
1940								9,167,279
1940S								4,550,000
1941								24,207,412
1941D								11,248,400
1941S								8,098,000
1942								47,839,120
1942D								10,973,800
1942S								12,708,000
1943								53,190,000
1943D								11,346,000
1943S								13,450,000
1944								28,206,000
1944D								9,769,000
1944S								8,904,000
1945								31,502,000
1945D								9,966,800
1945S								10,156,000
1946								12,118,000
1946D								2,151,100
1946S								3,724,000
1947								4,094,000
1947D								3,900,600

FRANKLIN-LIBERTY BELL TYPE

	Good	V. Good	Fine	V. Fine	Ex. Fine	Unc.	Proof	QUANTITY MINTED
1948								3,006,814
1948D								4,028,600
1949								5,714,000
1949D								4,120,600
1949S								3,744,000
1950								7,793,509
1950D								8,031,600
1951								16,859,602

HALF DOLLARS

DATE	Good	V. Good	Fine	V. Fine	Ex. Fine	Unc.	Proof	QUANTITY MINTED
1951D								9,475,200
1951S								13,696,000
1952								21,274,073
1952D								25,395,600
1952S								5,526,000
1953								2,796,920
1953D								20,900,400
1953S								4,148,000
1954								13,421,503
1954D								25,445,580
1954S								4,993,400
1955								2,876,381
1956								4,701,384
1957								6,361,952
1957D								19,966,850
1958								4,917,652
1958D								23,962,412
1959								7,349,291
1959D								13,053,750
1960								7,715,602
1960D								18,215,812
1961								11,318,244
1961D								20,276,442
1962								12,932,019
1962D								35,473,281
1963								25,239,645
1963D								67,069,292

KENNEDY TYPE

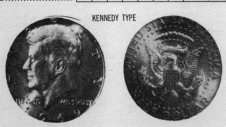

DATE	Good	V. Good	Fine	V. Fine	Ex. Fine	Unc.	Proof	QUANTITY MINTED
1964								277,254,766
1964D								156,205,446

CLAD HALVES (40% SILVER CONTENT)

DATE	Good	V. Good	Fine	V. Fine	Ex. Fine	Unc.	Proof	QUANTITY MINTED
1965								65,879,366
1966								108,984,932
1967								295,046,978
1968D								246,951,930
1968S Proof Only								3,041,509
1969D								129,881,800

HALF DOLLARS

DATE	Good	V. Good	Fine	V. Fine	Ex. Fine	Unc.	Proof	QUANTITY MINTED
1969S Proof Only								2,934,631
1970S Proof Only								
1971								
1971D								
1971S								

DOLLARS

DRAPED BUST TYPE

	Good	V. Good	Fine	V. Fine	Ex. Fine	Unc.	Proof	
1794 Flowing Hair								1,758
1795 Flowing Hair								184,013
1795 Draped Bust								203,033
1796 All Kinds								72,920
1797 All Kinds								7,776
1798 All Kinds								327,536

HERALDIC EAGLE REVERSE

	Good	V. Good	Fine	V. Fine	Ex. Fine	Unc.	Proof	
1798 part of								327,536
1799 All Kinds...........								423,515
1800.................								220,920
1801.................								54,454
1802.................								41,650
1803.................								85,634

DOLLARS

DATE

	Good	V. Good	Fine	V. Fine	Ex. Fine	Unc.	Proof	QUANTITY MINTED

LIBERTY SEATED TYPE

DATE	Good	V. Good	Fine	V. Fine	Ex. Fine	Unc.	Proof	QUANTITY MINTED
1840								61,005
1841								173,000
1842								184,618
1843								165,100
1844								20,000
1845								24,500
1846								110,600
1846O								59,000
1847								140,750
1848								15,000
1849								62,600
1850								7,500
1850O								40,000
1851 Original								1,300
1852 Original								1,100
1853								46,110
1854								33,140
1855								26,000
1856								63,500
1857								94,000
1859								256,500
1859O								360,000
1859S								20,000
1860								218,930
1860O								515,000
1861								78,500
1862								12,090
1863								27,660
1864								31,170
1865								47,000
WITH MOTTO ABOVE EAGLE								
1866								49,625
1867								47,525
1868								162,700
1869								424,300

DOLLARS

DATE	Good	V. Good	Fine	V. Fine	Ex. Fine	Unc.	Proof	QUANTITY MINTED
1870....................								416,000
1870CC..................								12,462
1871....................								1,074,760
1871CC..................								1,376
1872....................								1,106,450
1872CC..................								3,150
1872S								9,000
1873....................								293,600
1873CC..................								2,300
1873S Unknown.........								700

LIBERTY HEAD (MORGAN)

	Good	V. Good	Fine	V. Fine	Ex. Fine	Unc.	Proof	QUANTITY MINTED
1878 All Kinds...........								10,509,550
1878CC..................								2,212,000
1878S								9,774,000
1879....................								14,807,100
1879CC..................								756,000
1879O...................								2,887,000
1879S All Kinds								9,110,000
1880 All Kinds...........								12,601,355
1880CC All Kinds								591,000
1880O...................								5,305,000
1880S								8,900,000
1881....................								9,163,975
1881CC..................								296,000
1881O...................								5,708,000
1881S								12,760,000
1882....................								11,101,000
1882CC..................								1,133,000
1882O All Kinds								6,090,000
1882S								9,250,000
1883....................								12,291,039
1883CC..................								1,204,000
1883O...................								8,725,000
1883S								6,250,000
1884....................								14,070,875
1884CC..................								1,136,000

DOLLARS

DATE	Good	V. Good	Fine	V. Fine	Ex. Fine	Unc.	Proof	QUANTITY MINTED
1884O								9,730,000
1884S								3,200,000
1885								17,787,767
1885CC								228,000
1885O								9,185,000
1885S								1,497,000
1886								19,963,886
1886O								10,710,000
1886S								750,000
1887								20,290,710
1887O								11,550,000
1887S								1,771,000
1888								19,183,833
1888O								12,150,000
1888S								657,000
1889								21,726,811
1889CC								350,000
1889O								11,875,000
1889S								700,000
1890								16,802,590
1890CC								2,309,041
1890O								10,701,000
1890S								8,230,373
1891								8,694,206
1891CC								1,618,000
1891O								7,954,529
1891S								5,296,000
1892								1,037,245
1892CC								1,352,000
1892O								2,744,000
1892S								1,200,000
1893								378,792
1893CC								677,000
1893O								300,000
1893S								100,000
1894								110,972
1894O								1,723,000
1894S								1,260,000
1895								12,880
1895O								450,000
1895S								400,000
1896								9,976,762
1896O								4,900,000
1896S								5,000,000
1897								2,822,731
1897O								4,004,000
1897S								5,825,000
1898								5,884,735
1898O								4,440,000
1898S								4,102,000
1899								330,846

DOLLARS

DATE	Good	V. Good	Fine	V. Fine	Ex. Fine	Unc.	Proof	QUANTITY MINTED
1899O								12,290,000
1899S								2,562,000
1900								8,830,912
1900O								12,590,000
1900S								3,540,000
1901								6,962,813
1901O								13,320,000
1901S								2,284,000
1902								7,994,777
1902O								8,636,000
1902S								1,530,000
1903								4,652,755
1903O								4,450,000
1903S								1,241,000
1904								2,788,650
1904O								3,720,000
1904S								2,304,000
1921								44,690,000
1921D								20,345,000
1921S								21,695,000

PEACE TYPE

DATE	Good	V. Good	Fine	V. Fine	Ex. Fine	Unc.	Proof	QUANTITY MINTED
1921								1,006,473
1922								51,737,000
1922D								15,063,000
1922S								17,475,000
1923								30,800,000
1923D								6,811,000
1923S								19,020,000
1924								11,811,000
1924S								1,728,000
1925								10,198,000
1925S								1,610,000
1926								1,939,000
1926D								2,348,700
1926S								6,980,000
1927								848,000

DOLLARS

DATE	Good	V. Good	Fine	V. Fine	Ex. Fine	Unc.	Proof	QUANTITY MINTED
1927D...............								1,268,900
1927S...............								866,000
1928...............								360,649
1928S...............								1,632,000
1934...............								954,057
1934D...............								1,569,500
1934S...............								1,011,000
1935...............								1,576,000
1935S...............								1,964,000

TRADE DOLLARS

	Good	V. Good	Fine	V. Fine	Ex. Fine	Unc.	Proof	
1873...............								397,500
1873CC...............								124,500
1873S...............								703,000
1874...............								987,800
1874CC...............								1,373,200
1874S...............								2,549,000
1875...............								218,900
1875CC...............								1,573,700
1875S...............								4,487,000
1876...............								456,150
1876CC...............								509,000
1876S...............								5,227,000
1877...............								3,039,710
1877CC...............								534,000
1877S...............								9,519,000
1878 Proof Only								900
1878CC...............								97,000
1878S...............								4,162,000
1879 Proof Only								1,541
1880...............								1,987
1881...............								960
1882...............								1,097
1883...............								979
1884...............								10
1885...............								5

DOLLARS

DATE	Good	V. Good	Fine	V. Fine	Ex. Fine	Unc.	Proof	QUANTITY MINTED
1971								
1971D								
1971 S								

EISENHOWER DOLLAR

COMMEMORATIVE SILVER COINS

DATE		Ex. Fine	Unc.	QUANTITY MINTED
1892	Columbian Exposition			950,000
1893	Columbian Exposition			1,550,405
1893	Isabella Quarter Dollar			24,214
1900	Lafayette Dollar			36,026
1915S	Panama-Pacific Exposition			27,134
1918	Illinois Centennial			100,058
1920	Maine Centennial			50,028
1921	Missouri Centennial			15,428
1921	Missouri Centennial, 2★4 in Field			5,000
1920	Pilgrim Tercentenary			152,212
1921	Pilgrim Tercentenary			20,053
1921	Alabama Centennial			59,038
1921	Ala. Centennial, 2 x 2 in Obv. Field			6,006
1922	Grant Memorial			67,405
1922	Grant Memorial, Star in Obv. Field			4,256
1923S	Monroe Doctrine Centennial			274,077
1924	Huguenot-Walloon Tercentenary			142,080
1925	Lexington-Concord Sesquicent			162,013
1925	Stone Mountain Memorial			1,314,709
1925S	California Diamond Jubilee			86,594
1925S	Fort Vancouver Centennial			14,994
1926	Sesquicent. of American Independ.			141,120
1926	Oregon Trail Memorial			47,955
1926S	Oregon Trail Memorial			83,055
1928	Oregon Trail Memorial			6,028
1933D	Oregon Trail Memorial			5,008
1934D	Oregon Trail Memorial			7,006
1936	Oregon Trail Memorial			10,006
1936S	Oregon Trail Memorial			5,006
1937D	Oregon Trail Memorial			12,008

COMMEMORATIVE SILVER COINS

DATE		Ex. Fine	Unc.	QUANTITY MINTED
1938	Oregon Trail Memorial			6,006
1938D	Oregon Trail Memorial			6,005
1938S	Oregon Trail Memorial			6,006
1939	Oregon Trail Memorial			3,004
1939D	Oregon Trail Memorial			3,004
1939S	Oregon Trail Memorial			3,005
1927	Vermont Sesquicent. (Bennington).			28,162
1928	Hawaiian Sesquicentennial			10,008
1934	Maryland Tercentenary			25,015
1934	Texas Centennial			61,350
1935	Texas Centennial			9,994
1935D	Texas Centennial			10,007
1935S	Texas Centennial			10,008
1936	Texas Centennial			8,911
1936D	Texas Centennial			9,039
1936S	Texas Centennial			9,064
1937	Texas Centennial			6,571
1937D	Texas Centennial			6,605
1937S	Texas Centennial			6,637
1938	Texas Centennial			3,780
1938D	Texas Centennial			3,775
1938S	Texas Centennial			3,816
1934	Daniel Boone Bicentennial			10,007
1935	Daniel Boone Bicentennial			10,010
1935D	Daniel Boone Bicentennial			5,005
1935S	Daniel Boone Bicentennial			5,005
1935	Daniel Boone Bicent., 1934 on Rev.			10,008
1935D	Daniel Boone Bicent., 1934 on Rev.			2,003
1935S	Daniel Boone Bicent., 1934 on Rev.			2,004
1936	Daniel Boone Bicent., 1934 on Rev.			12,012
1936D	Daniel Boone Bicent., 1934 on Rev.			5,005
1936S	Daniel Boone Bicent., 1934 on Rev.			5,006
1937	Daniel Boone Bicent., 1934 on Rev.			9,810
1937D	Daniel Boone Bicent., 1934 on Rev.			2,506
1937S	Daniel Boone Bicent., 1934 on Rev.			2,506
1938	Daniel Boone Bicent., 1934 on Rev.			2,100
1938D	Daniel Boone Bicent., 1934 on Rev.			2,100
1938S	Daniel Boone Bicent., 1934 on Rev.			2,100
1935	Connecticut Tercentenary			25,018
1935	Arkansas Centennial			13,012
1935D	Arkansas Centennial			5,505
1935S	Arkansas Centennial			5,506
1936	Arkansas Centennial			9,660
1936D	Arkansas Centennial			9,660
1936S	Arkansas Centennial			9,662
1937	Arkansas Centennial			5,505
1937D	Arkansas Centennial			5,505
1937S	Arkansas Centennial			5,506
1938	Arkansas Centennial			3,156

COMMEMORATIVE SILVER COINS

DATE	Ex. Fine	Unc.	QUANTITY MINTED
1938D Arkansas Centennial			3,155
1938S Arkansas Centennial			3,156
1939 Arkansas Centennial			2,104
1939D Arkansas Centennial			2,104
1939S Arkansas Centennial			2,105
1935 Hudson, N. Y. Sesquicentennial			10,008
1935S San Diego, Cal.-Pacific Exposition			70,132
1936D San Diego, Cal.-Pacific Exposition			30,092
1935 Old Spanish Trail, 1535-1935			10,008
1936 Rhode Island Tercentenary			20,013
1936D Rhode Island Tercentenary			15,010
1936S Rhode Island Tercentenary			15,011
1936 Cleveland, Great Lakes Exposition			50,030
1936 Wisconsin Centennial			25,015
1936 Cincinnati Musical Center			5,005
1936D Cincinnati Musical Center			5,005
1936S Cincinnati Musical Center			5,006
1936 Long Island Tercentenary			81,826
1936 York County, Maine Tercentenary			25,015
1936 Bridgeport, Connecticut Centennial			25,015
1936 Lynchburg, Virginia Sesquicent....			20,013
1936 Elgin, Illinois Centennial			20,015
1936 Albany, New York Charter			17,671
1936S San Francisco-Oakland Bay Bridge			71,424
1936 Columbia, S. C. Sesquicentennial			9,007
1936D Columbia, S. C. Sesquicentennial..			8,009
1936S Columbia, S. C. Sesquicentennial..			8,007
1936 Arkansas Centennial (Robinson) ...			25,265
1936 Delaware Tercentenary			20,993
1936 Battle of Gettysburg, 1863-1938 ...			26,928
1936 Norfolk, Virginia Bicentennial			16,936
1937 Roanoke Island, N. C., 1587-1937 .			29,030
1937 Battle of Antietam, 1862-1937			18,028
1938 New Rochelle, N. Y., 1688-1938 ...			15,266
1946 Iowa Centennial			100,057
1946 Booker T. Washington Memorial ..			1,000,546
1946D Booker T. Washington Memorial ..			200,113
1946S Booker T. Washington Memorial ..			500,279
1947 Booker T. Washington Memorial ..			100,017
1947D Booker T. Washington Memorial ..			100,017
1947S Booker T. Washington Memorial ..			100,017
1948 Booker T. Washington Memorial ..			8,005
1948D Booker T. Washington Memorial ..			8,005
1948S Booker T. Washington Memorial ..			8,005
1949 Booker T. Washington Memorial ..			6,004
1949D Booker T. Washington Memorial ..			6,004
1949S Booker T. Washington Memorial ..			6,004
1950 Booker T. Washington Memorial ..			6,004
1950D Booker T. Washington Memorial ..			6,004
1950S Booker T. Washington Memorial ..			512,091

COMMEMORATIVE SILVER COINS

DATE	Ex. Fine	Unc.	QUANTITY MINTED
1951 Booker T. Washington Memorial ..			510,082
1951D Booker T. Washington Memorial ..			7,004
1951S Booker T. Washington Memorial ..			7,004
1951 Washington-Carver....................			110,018
1951D Washington-Carver....................			10,004
1951S Washington-Carver....................			10,004
1952 Washington-Carver....................			2,006,292
1952D Washington-Carver....................			8,006
1952S Washington-Carver....................			8,006
1953 Washington-Carver....................			8,003
1953D Washington-Carver....................			8,003
1953S Washington-Carver....................			108,020
1954 Washington-Carver....................			12,006
1954D Washington-Carver....................			12,006
1954S Washington-Carver....................			122,024

GOLD COMMEMORATIVES

DATE	Good	V. Good	Fine	V. Fine	Ex. Fine	Unc.	Proof	QUANTITY MINTED
1903 .... Jefferson Dollar								17,500
1903 .... McKinley Dollar								17,500
1904 .... Lewis and Clark Dollar								10,025
1905 .... Lewis and Clark Dollar								10,041
1915S .... Panama Pacific Dollar								15,000
1915S .... Panama Pacific $2.50								6,749
1915S .... Pan Pacific $50 Rd								483
1915S .... Pan Pacific $50 Oct								645
1916 .... McKinley Dollar								9,977
1917 .... McKinley Dollar								10,000

GOLD COMMEMORATIVES

DATE	Good	V. Good	Fine	V. Fine	Ex. Fine	Unc.	Proof	QUANTITY MINTED
1922 . . . . Grant Dollar with star								5,016
1922 . . . . Grant Dollar no star								5,000
1926 . . . . Phila Sesqui. $2.50								46,019

GOLD DOLLARS

 LIBERTY HEAD

DATE	Good	V. Good	Fine	V. Fine	Ex. Fine	Unc.	Proof	QUANTITY MINTED
1849 Both Kinds . . .								688,567
1849C Both Kinds . .								11,634
1849D								21,588
1849O								215,000
1850								481,953
1850C								6,966
1850D								8,382
1850O								14,000
1851								3,317,671
1851C								41,267
1851D								9,882
1851O								290,000
1852								2,045,351
1852C								9,434
1852D								6,360
1852O								140,000
1853								4,076,051
1853C								11,515
1853D								6,583
1853O								290,000
1854 Lg. Head . . . . . 1854 Sm. Head								736,709
1854D			'					2,935
1854S Lg. Head								14,632
1854 Sm. Head . . .								902,736
1855 . . . . . ↓								758,269
1855C								9,803
1855D . . . . ↓								1,811
1855O . . . . ↓								55,000
1856S								24,600

GOLD DOLLARS

DATE	Good	V. Good	Fine	V. Fine	Ex. Fine	Unc.	Proof	QUANTITY MINTED
1856 lg. Head								1,762,936
1856D								1,460
1857								774,789
1857C								13,280
1857D								3,533
1857S								10,000
1858								117,995
1858D								3,477
1858S								10,000
1859								168,244
1859C								5,235
1859D								4,952
1859S								15,000
1860								36,668
1860D								1,566
1860S								13,000
1861								527,499
1861D								
1862								1,361,392
1863								6,250
1864								5,950
1865								3,725
1866								7,200
1867								5,250
1868								10,525
1869								5,925
1870								6,335
1870S								3,000
1871								3,930
1872								3,530
1873 Both Kinds ...								125,125
1874								198,820
1875								420
1876								3,245
1877								3,920
1878								3,020
1879								3,030
1880								1,636
1881								7,700
1882								5,120
1883								11,010
1884								6,230
1885								12,260
1886								6,016
1887								8,543
1888								165,822
1889								30,729

QUARTER EAGLES
($2.50 Gold Pieces)

DATE	Good	V. Good	Fine	V. Fine	Ex. Fine	Unc.	Proof	QUANTITY MINTED
CAPPED BUST TYPE								
1796 No Stars								965
1796 With Stars ...								430
1797								428
1798								1,089
1802 over 1								3,036
1804								3,327
1805								1,781
1806 over 4								} 1,616
1806 over 5								
1807								6,812
1808 Faces Left								2,710
1821 reduced size ..								6,448
1824 over 21								2,600
1825								4,434
1826 over 25								760
1827								2,800
1829								3,403
1830								4,540
1831								4,520
1832								4,400
1833								4,160
1834 with motto...								4,000
LIBERTY HEAD WITH RIBBON TYPE								
1834 without motto								112,234
1835								131,402
1836								547,986
1837								45,080
1838								47,030
1838C								7,885
1839								27,021
1839C								18,173
1839D								13,674
1839O								17,781
CORONET TYPE								

DATE	Good	V. Good	Fine	V. Fine	Ex. Fine	Unc.	Proof	QUANTITY MINTED
1840								18,859
1840C								12,838
1840D								3,532
1840O								33,575
1841 Proof Only ...								
1841C								10,297

QUARTER EAGLES
($2.50 Gold Pieces)

DATE	Good	V. Good	Fine	V. Fine	Ex. Fine	Unc.	Proof	QUANTITY MINTED
1841D								4,164
1842								2,823
1842C								6,737
1842D								4,643
1842O								19,800
1843								100,546
1843C Lg. Date								⎱ 26,096
1843C Sm. Date								⎰
1843D small date ..								36,209
1843O Lg. Date								76,200
1843O Sm. Date								288,000
1844								6,784
1844C								11,622
1844D								17,332
1845								91,051
1845D								19,460
1845O								4,000
1846								21,598
1846C								4,808
1846D								19,303
1846O								66,000
1847								29,814
1847C								23,226
1847D								15,784
1847O								124,000
1848								7,497
1848								1,389
CAL over eagle								
1848C								16,788
1848D								13,771
1849								23,294
1849C								10,220
1849D								10,945
1850								252,923
1850C								9,148
1850D								12,148
1850O								84,000
1851								1,372,748
1851C								14,923
1851D								11,264
1851O								148,000
1852								1,159,681
1852C								9,772
1852D								4,078
1852O								140,000
1853								1,404,668
1853D								3,178
1854								596,258
1854C								7,295

QUARTER EAGLES
($2.50 Gold Pieces)

DATE	Good	V. Good	Fine	V. Fine	Ex. Fine	Unc.	Proof	QUANTITY MINTED
1854D								1,760
1854O								153,000
1854S								246
1855								235,480
1855C								3,677
1855D								1,123
1856								384,240
1856C								7,913
1856D								874
1856O								21,100
1856S								71,120
1857								214,130
1857D								2,364
1857O								34,000
1857S								69,000
1858								47,377
1858C								9,056
1859								39,444
1859D								2,244
1859S								15,200
1860								22,675
1860C								7,469
1860S								35,600
1861								1,283,878
1861S								24,000
1862								98,543
1862S								8,000
1863 proofs only								30
1863S								10,800
1864								2,874
1865								1,545
1865S								23,376
1866								3,110
1866S								38,960
1867								3,250
1867S								28,000
1868								3,625
1868S								34,000
1869								4,345
1869S								29,500
1870								4,555
1870S								16,000
1871								5,350
1871S								22,000
1872								3,030
1872S								18,000
1873 Both Kinds								178,025
1873S								27,000
1874								3,940
1875								420

QUARTER EAGLES
($2.50 Gold Pieces)

DATE	Good	V. Good	Fine	V. Fine	Ex. Fine	Unc.	Proof	QUANTITY MINTED
1875S								11,600
1876								4,221
1876S								5,000
1877								1,652
1877S								35,400
1878								286,260
1878S								178,000
1879								88,990
1879S								43,500
1880								2,996
1881								690
1882								4,040
1883								2,000
1884								2,020
1885								887
1886								4,088
1887								6,282
1888								16,098
1889								17,648
1890								8,813
1891								11,040
1892								2,545
1893								30,106
1894								4,122
1895								6,119
1896								19,202
1897								29,904
1898								24,165
1899								27,350
1900								67,205
1901								91,323
1902								133,733
1903								201,257
1904								160,960
1905								217,944
1906								176,490
1907								336,448

INDIAN HEAD TYPE

	Good	V. Good	Fine	V. Fine	Ex. Fine	Unc.	Proof	QUANTITY MINTED
1908								565,057
1909								441,899
1910								492,682
1911								704,191

QUARTER EAGLES
($2.50 Gold Pieces)

DATE	Good	V. Good	Fine	V. Fine	Ex. Fine	Unc.	Proof	QUANTITY MINTED
1911D								55,680
1912								616,197
1913								722,165
1914								240,117
1914D								448,000
1915								606,100
1925D								578,000
1926								446,000
1927								388,000
1928								416,000
1929								532,000

THREE DOLLAR GOLD PIECES

DATE	Good	V. Good	Fine	V. Fine	Ex. Fine	Unc.	Proof	QUANTITY MINTED
1854								138,618
1854D								1,120
1854O								24,000
1855								50,555
1855S								6,600
1856								26,010
1856S								34,500
1857								20,891
1857S								14,000
1858								2,133
1859								15,638
1860								7,155
1860S								7,000
1861								6,072
1862								5,785
1863								5,039
1864								2,680
1865								1,165
1866								4,030
1867								2,650
1868								4,875
1869								2,525
1870								3,535
1871								1,330
1872								2,030
1873 proofs only ..								25
1874								41,820
1875 proofs only...								20
1876 proofs only ..								45

THREE DOLLAR GOLD PIECES

DATE	Good	V. Good	Fine	V. Fine	Ex. Fine	Unc.	Proof	QUANTITY MINTED
1877								1,488
1878								82,324
1879								3,030
1880								1,036
1881								550
1882								1,575
1883								990
1884								1,106
1885								910
1886								1,142
1887								6,160
1888								5,291
1889								2,429

$4.00 GOLD OR "STELLA"

	Good	V. Good	Fine	V. Fine	Ex. Fine	Unc.	Proof	
1879 Flowing hair, Proof								415
1879 Coiled hair, Proof								10
1880 Flowing hair, Proof								15
1880 Coiled hair, Proof								10

$5.00 GOLD PIECES

1795 Small eagle								8,707
1795 Large eagle								

$5.00 GOLD PIECES

DATE	Good	V. Good	Fine	V. Fine	Ex. Fine	Unc.	Proof	QUANTITY MINTED
BUST FACING RIGHT								
1796 Small eagle . . .								6,196
1797 Large eagle . . . over 95								part of 3609
1797 Sm. Eagle								part of 3609
1797								part of 3609
1798 Lg. Eagle								24,867
1799								7,451
1800								37,620
1802 over 1								53,176
1803 over 2								33,506
1804								30,475
1805								33,183
1806								64,093
1807								3z,430
Bust facing right								

BUST FACING LEFT

DATE	Good	V. Good	Fine	V. Fine	Ex. Fine	Unc.	Proof	QUANTITY MINTED
1807 . . . . Bust facing left								51,600
1808 . . . . 1808 8 over 7								55,578
1809 9 over 8								33,875
1810 All Kinds								100,287
1811 Both Kinds								99,581
1812								58,087
1813								95,428
1814 over 13								15,454
1815								635
1818								48,588
1819								51,723
1820 All Kinds								263,806
1821								34,641
1822				V. Rare				17,796
1823								14,485
1824								17,340
1825 over 21								29,060

$5.00 GOLD PIECES

DATE	Good	V. Good	Fine	V. Fine	Ex. Fine	Unc.	Proof	QUANTITY MINTED
1825 over 24								
1826								18,069
1827								24,913
1828 Both Kinds . . .								28,029
1829 V. Rare								57,442
1830 Both Kinds . . .								126,351
1831								140,594
1832								157,487
1833								193,630
1834 Motto All Kinds								50,141

NO MOTTO   CORONET TYPE

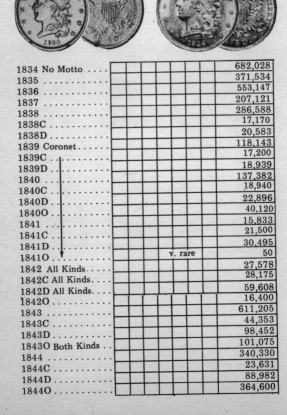

	Good	V. Good	Fine	V. Fine	Ex. Fine	Unc.	Proof	QUANTITY MINTED
1834 No Motto								682,028
1835								371,534
1836								553,147
1837								207,121
1838								286,588
1838C								17,170
1838D								20,583
1839 Coronet . . . . . ·								118,143
1839C								17,200
1839D								18,939
1840								137,382
1840C								18,940
1840D								22,896
1840O								40,120
1841								15,833
1841C								21,500
1841D								30,495
1841O					v. rare			50
1842 All Kinds								27,578
1842C All Kinds								28,175
1842D All Kinds								59,608
1842O								16,400
1843								611,205
1843C								44,353
1843D								98,452
1843O Both Kinds . .								101,075
1844								340,330
1844C								23,631
1844D								88,982
1844O								364,600

$5.00 GOLD PIECES

DATE	Good	V. Good	Fine	V. Fine	Ex. Fine	Unc.	Proof	QUANTITY MINTED
1845								417,099
1845D								90,629
1845O								41,000
1846								395,942
1846C								12,995
1846D								80,294
1846O								58,000
1847								915,981
1847C								84,151
1847D								64,405
1847O								12,000
1848								260,775
1848C								64,472
1848D								47,465
1849								133,070
1849C								64,823
1849D								39,036
1850								64,491
1850C								63,591
1850D								43,975
1851								377,505
1851C								49,176
1851D								62,710
1851O								41,000
1852								573,901
1852C								72,574
1852D								91,580
1853								305,770
1853C								65,571
1853D								89,678
1854								160,675
1854C								39,291
1854D								56,413
1854O								46,000
1854S				V. Rare				268
1855								117,098
1855C								39,788
1855D								22,432
1855O								11,100
1855S								61,000
1856								197,990
1856C								28,457
1856D								19,786
1856O								10,000
1856S								105,100
1857								98,188
1857C								31,360
1857D								17,046
1857O								13,000

$5.00 GOLD PIECES

DATE	Good	V. Good	Fine	V. Fine	Ex. Fine	Unc.	Proof	QUANTITY MINTED
1857S								87,000
1858								15,136
1858C								38,856
1858D								15,362
1858S								18,600
1859								16,814
1859C								31,847
1859D								10,366
1859S								13,220
1860								19,825
1860C								14,813
1860D								14,635
1860S								21,200
1861								688,150
1861C								6,879
1861D								1,597
1861S								18,000
1862								4,465
1862S								9,500
1863								2,472
1863S								17,000
1864								4,220
1864S								3,888
1865								1,295
1865S								27,612
1866S no motto ... (all kinds)								43,920 99,000
1866 Motto								6,730
1866S . ↓								34,920
1867								6,920
1867S								29,000
1868								5,725
1868S								52,000
1869								1,785
1869S								31,000
1870								4,035
1870CC								7,675
1870S								17,000
1871								3,230
1871CC								20,770
1871S								25,000
1872								1,690
1872CC								16,980
1872S								36,400
1873 Both Kinds ...								112,505
1873CC								7,416
1873S								31,000
1874								3,508
1874CC								21,198

$5.00 GOLD PIECES

DATE	Good	V. Good	Fine	V. Fine	Ex. Fine	Unc.	Proof	QUANTITY MINTED
1874S								16,000
1875								220
1875CC								11,828
1875S								9,000
1876								1,477
1876CC								6,887
1876S								4,000
1877								1,152
1877CC								8,380
1877S								26,700
1878								131,740
1878CC								9,054
1878S								144,700
1879								301,950
1879CC								17,281
1879S								426,200
1880								3,166,436
1880CC								51,017
1880S								1,348,900
1881								5,708,800
1881CC								13,886
1881S								969,000
1882								2,514,560
1882CC								82,817
1882S								969,999
1883								233,460
1883CC								12,958
1883S								83,200
1884								191,075
1884CC								16,402
1884S								177,000
1885								601,506
1885S								1,211,500
1886								388,432
1886S								3,268,000
1887 proofs only ..			V. Rare					87
1887S								1,912,000
1888								18,296
1888S								293,900
1889								7,565
1890								4,328
1890CC								53,800
1891								61,413
1891CC								208,000
1892								753,572
1892CC								82,968
1892O								10,000
1892S								298,400
1893								1,528,197
1893CC								60,000

$5.00 GOLD PIECES

DATE	Good	V. Good	Fine	V. Fine	Ex. Fine	Unc.	Proof	QUANTITY MINTED
1893O								110,000
1893S								224,000
1894								957,955
1894O								16,600
1894S								55,900
1895								1,345,936
1895S								112,000
1896								59,063
1896S								155,400
1897								867,883
1897S								354,000
1898								633,495
1898S								1,397,400
1899								1,710,729
1899S								1,545,000
1900								1,405,730
1900S								329,000
1901								616,040
1901S								3,648,000
1902								172,562
1902S								939,000
1903								227,024
1903S								1,855,000
1904								392,136
1904S								97,000
1905								302,308
1905S								880,700
1906								348,820
1906D								320,000
1906S								598,000
1907								626,192
1907D								888,000
1908								421,874

INDIAN HEAD TYPE

DATE	Good	V. Good	Fine	V. Fine	Ex. Fine	Unc.	Proof	QUANTITY MINTED
1908								578,012
1908D								148,000
1908S								82,000
1909								627,138
1909D								3,423,560
1909O								34,200
1909S								297,200

$5.00 GOLD PIECES

DATE	Good	V. Good	Fine	V. Fine	Ex. Fine	Unc.	Proof	QUANTITY MINTED
1910								604,250
1910D								193,600
1910S								770,200
1911								915,139
1911D								72,500
1911S								1,416,000
1912								790,144
1912S								392,000
1913								916,099
1913S								408,000
1914								247,125
1914D								247,000
1914S								263,000
1915								588,075
1915S								164,000
1916S								240,000
1929								662,000

EAGLES ($10.00 Gold Pieces)

	Good	V. Good	Fine	V. Fine	Ex. Fine	Unc.	Proof	
1795								5,580
1796								4,146
1797 small eagle								2,460
1797 large eagle								12,090
1798 over 97								1,750
1799 All Kinds								37,450
1800								5,999
1801								44,340
1803								15,000
1804								3,750

CORONET TYPE 1838 ON

	Good	V. Good	Fine	V. Fine	Ex. Fine	Unc.	Proof	
1838								7,200
1839 Both Kinds								38,248
1840								47,338
1841								63,131
1841O								2,500
1842 Both Kinds								81,507

EAGLES
($10.00 Gold Pieces)

DATE	Good	V. Good	Fine	V. Fine	Ex. Fine	Unc.	Proof	QUANTITY MINTED
1842O								27,400
1843								75,462
1843O								175,162
1844								6,361
1844O								118,700
1845								26,153
1845O								47,500
1846								20,095
1846O								81,780
1847								862,258
1847O								571,500
1848								145,484
1848O								35,850
1849								653,618
1849O								23,900
1850								291,451
1850O								57,500
1851								176,328
1851O								263,000
1852								263,106
1852O								18,000
1853								201,253
1853O								51,000
1854								54,250
1854O								52,500
1854S								123,826
1855								121,701
1855O								18,000
1855S								9,000
1856								60,490
1856O								14,500
1856S								68,000
1857								16,606
1857O								5,500
1857S								26,000
1858								2,521
1858O								20,000
1858S								11,800
1859								16,093
1859O								2,300
1859S								7,000
1860								15,105
1860O								11,100
1860S								5,000
1861								113,233
1861S								15,500
1862								10,995
1862S								12,500
1863								1,248

EAGLES
($10.00 Gold Pieces)

DATE

	Good	V. Good	Fine	V. Fine	Ex. Fine	Unc.	Proof	QUANTITY MINTED

CORONET TYPE 1838–1907
MOTTO OVER EAGLE ADDED 1866 ON

DATE	Good	V. Good	Fine	V. Fine	Ex. Fine	Unc.	Proof	QUANTITY MINTED
1863S								10,000
1864								3,580
1864S								2,500
1865								4,005
1865S All Kinds								16,700
1866S part of No Motto								20,000
1866 Motto								3,780
1866S part of								20,000
1867								3,140
1867S								9,000
1868								10,655
1868S								13,500
1869								1,855
1869S								6,430
1870								4,025
1870CC								5,908
1870S								8,000
1871								1,820
1871CC								7,185
1871S								16,500
1872								1,650
1872CC								5,500
1872S								17,300
1873								825
1873CC								4,543
1873S								12,000
1874								53,160
1874CC								16,767
1874S								10,000
1875								120
1875CC								7,715
1876								732
1876CC								4,696
1876S								5,000
1877								817

EAGLES
($10.00 Gold Pieces)

DATE	Good	V. Good	Fine	V. Fine	Ex. Fine	Unc.	Proof	QUANTITY MINTED
1877CC								3,332
1877S								17,000
1878								73,800
1878CC								3,244
1878S								26,100
1879								384,770
1879CC								1,762
1879O								1,500
1879S								224,000
1880								1,644,876
1880CC								11,190
1880O								9,200
1880S								506,250
1881								3,877,260
1883CC								24,015
1881O								8,350
1881S								970,000
1882								2,324,480
1882CC								6,764
1882O								10,820
1882S								132,000
1883								208,740
1883CC								12,000
1883O								800
1883S								38,000
1884								76,905
1884CC								9,925
1884S								124,250
1885								253,527
1885S								228,000
1886								236,160
1886S								826,000
1887								53,680
1887S								817,000
1888								132,996
1888O								21,335
1888S								648,700
1889								4,485
1889S								425,400
1890								58,043
1890CC								17,500
1891								91,868
1891CC								103,732
1892								797,552
1892CC								40,000
1892O								28,688
1892S								115,500
1893								1,840,895

EAGLES
($10.00 Gold Pieces)

DATE	Good	V. Good	Fine	V. Fine	Ex. Fine	Unc.	Proof	QUANTITY MINTED
1893CC								14,000
1893O								17,000
1893S								141,350
1894								2,470,778
1894O								107,500
1894S								25,000
1895								567,826
1895O								98,000
1895S								49,000
1896								76,348
1896S								123,750
1897								1,000,159
1897O								42,500
1897S								234,750
1898								812,197
1898S								473,600
1899								1,262,305
1899O								37,047
1899S								841,000
1900								293,960
1900S								81,000
1901								1,718,825
1901O								72,041
1901S								2,812,750
1902								82,513
1902S								469,500
1903								125,926
1903O								112,771
1903S								538,000
1904								162,038
1904O								108,950
1905								201,078
1905S								369,250
1906								165,497
1906D								981,000
1906O								86,895
1906S								457,000
1907 L								1,203,973
1907D								1,030,000
1907S								210,500

EAGLES
($10.00 Gold Pieces)

	Good	V. Good	Fine	V. Fine	Ex. Fine	Unc.	Proof	QUANTITY MINTED

INDIAN HEAD TYPE
MOTTO ADDED 1908

DATE

DATE	Good	V. Good	Fine	V. Fine	Ex. Fine	Unc.	Proof	QUANTITY MINTED
1907 Indian, regular								239,406
1907 Wire edge, ... periods								500
1907 Rolled edge, .. periods								42
1908 No motto								33,500
1908 Motto								341,486
1908D No motto ..								210,000
1908D Motto								836,500
1908S Motto								59,853
1909								184,860
1909D								121,540
1909S								292,350
1910								318,704
1910D								2,356,640
1910S								811,000
1911								505,595
1911D								30,100
1911S								51,000
1912								405,083
1912S								300,000
1913								442,071
1913S								66,000
1914								151,050
1914D								343,500
1914S								208,000
1915								351,075
1915S								59,000
1916S								138,500
1920S								126,500
1926								1,014,000
1930S								96,000
1932								4,463,000
1933								312,500

DOUBLE EAGLES
($20.00 Gold Pieces)

DATE	Good	V. Good	Fine	V. Fine	Ex. Fine	Unc.	Proof	QUANTITY MINTED

LIBERTY HEAD

DATE	Good	V. Good	Fine	V. Fine	Ex. Fine	Unc.	Proof	QUANTITY MINTED
1850								1,170,261
1850O								141,000
1851								2,087,155
1851O								315,000
1852								2,053,026
1852O								190,000
1853								1,261,326
1853O								71,000
1854								757,899
1854O								3,250
1854S								141,468
1855								364,666
1855O								8,000
1855S								879,675
1856								329,878
1856O								2,250
1856S								1,189,750
1857								439,375
1857O								30,000
1857S								970,500
1858								211,714
1858O								35,250
1858S								846,710
1859								43,597
1859O								9,100
1859S								636,445
1860								577,670
1860O								6,600
1860S								544,950
1861								2,976,453
1861O								5,000
1861S								768,000
1862								92,133
1862S								854,173

DOUBLE EAGLES
($20.00 Gold Pieces)

DATE	Good	V. Good	Fine	V. Fine	Ex. Fine	Unc.	Proof	QUANTITY MINTED
1863								142,790
1863S								966,570
1864								204,285
1864S								793,660
1865								351,200
1865S								1,042,500
1866S No motto ... part of								842,250

MOTTO ABOVE EAGLE-TWENTY D. REVERSE

	Good	V. Good	Fine	V. Fine	Ex. Fine	Unc.	Proof	QUANTITY MINTED
1866 Motto								698,775
1866S part of ..... Motto (all kinds)								842,250
1867								251,065
1867S								920,750
1868								98,600
1868S								837,500
1869								175,155
1869S								686,750
1870								155,185
1870CC								3,789
1870S								982,000
1871								80,150
1871CC								14,687
1871S								928,000
1872								251,880
1872CC								29,650
1872S								780,000
1873								1,709,825
1873CC Both Kinds .								22,410
1873S								1,040,600
1874								366,800
1874CC...........								115,085
1874S								1,214,000
1875								295,740
1875CC								111,151
1875S								1,230,000
1876								583,905
1876CC								138,441
1876S								1,597,000

TWENTY DOLLARS REVERSE

	Good	V. Good	Fine	V. Fine	Ex. Fine	Unc.	Proof	QUANTITY MINTED
1877								397,670
1877CC								42,565
1877S								1,735,000
1878								543,645
1878CC								13,180
1878S								1,739,000
1879								207,630
1879CC								10,708

DOUBLE EAGLES
($20.00 Gold Pieces)

DATE	Good	V. Good	Fine	V. Fine	Ex. Fine	Unc.	Proof	QUANTITY MINTED
1879O								2,325
1879S								1,223,800
1880								51,456
1880S								836,000
1881								2,260
1881S								727,000
1882								630
1882CC								39,140
1882S								1,125,000
1883 proofs only								40
1883CC								59,962
1883S								1,189,000
1884 Proof Only								71
1884CC								81,139
1884S								916,000
1885								828
1885CC								9,450
1885S								683,500
1886								1,106
1887 proofs only								121
1887S								283,000
1888								226,266
1888S								859,600
1889								44,111
1889CC								30,945
1889S								774,700
1890								75,995
1890CC								91,209
1890S								802,750
1891								1,442
1891CC								5,000
1891S								1,288,125
1892								4,523
1892CC								27,265
1892S								930,150
1893								344,339
1893CC								18,402
1893S								966,175
1894								1,368,990
1894S								1,048,550
1895								1,114,656
1895S								1,143,500
1896								792,663
1896S								1,403,925
1897								1,383,261
1897S								1,470,250
1898								170,470
1898S								2,575,175

DOUBLE EAGLES
($20.00 Gold Pieces)

DATE	Good	V. Good	Fine	V. Fine	Ex. Fine	Unc.	Proof	QUANTITY MINTED
1899								1,669,384
1899S								2,010,300
1900								1,874,584
1900S								2,459,500
1901								111,526
1901S								1,596,000
1902								31,254
1902S								1,753,625
1903								287,428
1903S								954,000
1904								6,256,797
1904S								5,134,175
1905								59,011
1905S								1,813,000
1906								69,690
1906D								620,250
1906S								2,065,750
1907								1,451,864
1907D								842,250
1907S								2,165,800

	Good	V. Good	Fine	V. Fine	Ex. Fine	Unc.	Proof	QUANTITY MINTED
1907 MCMVII								11,250
1907								361,667
1908 No motto								4,271,551
1908 Motto								156,359
1908D No motto								663,750
1908D Motto								349,500
1908S Motto								22,000
1909								161,282
1909 9 over 8								
1909D								52,500
1909S								2,774,925
1910								482,167
1910D								429,000
1910S								2,128,250

DOUBLE EAGLES
($20.00 Gold Pieces)

DATE	Good	V. Good	Fine	V. Fine	Ex. Fine	Unc.	Proof	QUANTITY MINTED
1911								197,350
1911D								846,500
1911S								775,750
1912								149,824
1913								168,838
1913D								383,500
1913S								34,000
1914								95,320
1914D								453,000
1914S								1,498,000
1915								152,050
1915S								567,500
1916S								796,000
1920								228,250
1920S								558,000
1921								528,500
1922								1,375,500
1922S								2,658,000
1923								566,000
1923D								1,702,250
1924								4,323,500
1924D								3,049,500
1924S								2,927,500
1925								2,831,750
1925D								2,938,500
1925S								3,776,500
1926								816,750
1926D								481,000
1926S								2,041,500
1927								2,946,750
1927D								180,000
1927S								3,107,000
1928								8,816,000
1929								1,779,750
1930S								74,000
1931								2,938,250
1931D								106,500
1932								1,101,750

1933 No Record—Never Circulated

PROOF SETS

DATE	Proof	QUANTITY MINTED
1936		3,837
1937		5,542
1938		8,045
1939		8,795
1940		11,246
1941		15,287
1942		21,120
1950		51,386
1951		57,500
1952		81,890
1953		128,800
1954		233,300
1955		378,200
1956		669,384
1957		1,247,952
1958		875,652
1959		1,149,291
1960 Lg. Date 1¢ . . . 1960 Sm. Date 1¢		1,691,602
1961		3,028,244
1962		3,218,019
1963		3,075,645
1964		3,950,762
1968S		3,041,506
1969S		2,934,631
1970S		
1971S		

SPECIAL MINT SETS

DATE	Unc.	QUANTITY MINTED
1965		2,360,000
1966		2,261,583
1967		1,863,344